IRISH COUN...
AND RESTAU...

W9-CON-989

IRELAND'S BLUE BOOK is a unique Association comprising Ireland's most charming Country Manor Houses, Castles and Restaurants. The premises described in the Blue Book will appeal to the discerning visitor who is searching for high standards of traditional hospitality, accommodation and fine cuisine amidst the quiet beauty of rural Ireland.

If your choice is golf or beautiful scenery; mountains to climb; rivers and lakes to fish; miles and miles of golden beaches – they will be found close by to one or other of the Houses in the Association.

CHOOSING YOUR HOLIDAY!
The members of the Association are in four categories:
1. Country Houses with Restaurants open to non-residents.
2. Country Houses catering for residents only.
3. Restaurants with Accommodation.
4. Restaurants only.

You may choose to stay in a Grand Manor House, a friendly Country Home or a cosy Restaurant with Accommodation. No two properties are the same, each giving a different flavour and atmosphere and where you will experience genuine friendliness and old fashioned courtesy in warm and relaxing surroundings. The Blue Book also includes three of Dublin's finest restaurants for people wishing to dine in the city.

In the summaries of service, the price for bed and breakfast (B&B) is per person sharing for a double room/suite with bath/shower, unless otherwise stated. Some houses have a single room supplement. The price for dinner is an average one, and the dinner times refer to first and last orders. One or more European languages are spoken at most premises. Booking is essential.

Each property has its own reservation policy. When booking please check their individual deposit and cancellation policies. Charges may apply in respect of the full value of your booking. Also check that your travel insurance provides cover against cancellation charges. All members of the Association have individual brochures, which they will be happy to send on request.

Correspondence / Enquiries:

Ireland's Blue Book,
8 Mount Street Crescent,
Dublin 2,
Ireland.
Tel: +353-(0)1-6769914.
Fax: +353-(0)1-6314990.
E-Mail: mail@irelandsbluebook.com
Web Site: www.irelandsbluebook.com

RESTAURANTS ET HOTELS D'IRLANDE

L'Association "IRLAND'S BLUE BOOK" rassemble les meilleurs restaurants et hôtels de charme d'Irlande. Les établissements décrits ici séduiront le visiteur le plus exigeant, recherchant avec le raffinement de l'hospitalité traditionnelle un hébergement haut de gamme et une cuisine savoureuse dans le cadre magnifique et paisible de l'Irlande rurale.

Que vous soyez un passionné de golf, de randonnées en montagne, de pêche en lac ou en rivière, que vous vouliez simplement profiter de la beauté d'un paysage admirable, telles les plages immenses du littoral, vous trouverez nécessairement un des hôtels membres de l'Association dans l'endroit voulu.

CHOISIR VOTRE LIEU DE SÉJOUR

Les membres de l'Association sont regroupés en quatre catégories:
1. Hôtels avec restaurant ouvert aux non-résidents.
2. Hôtels avec restaurant réservé aux résidents.
3. Restaurants proposant un hébergement.
4. Restaurants seulement.

Vous pourrez, à votre guise, choisir de séjourner dans un somptueux manoir, une gentilhommière accueillante ou une confortable auberge au charme rustique. Chacun des établissements à son propre cachet, vous n'en trouverez pas deux pareils. Chacun vous offrira une atmosphère et un style différents. Mais tous vous réserveront un accueil amical, empreint de la traditionnelle courtoisie, dans un cadre chaleureux et paisible. Et vous trouverez un excellent restaurant même dans les coins les plus reculés de notre île. Le Blue Book comprend également trois des meilleurs restaurants de Dublin, pour ceux qui souhaitent dîner dans la ville.

Les prix sont indiqués ici, sauf mention contraire, par personne; ils comprennent une chambre pour deux avec salle de bains/douche et le petit déjeuner.

Le prix des repas est un prix moyen; les horaires donnés sont ceux des premières et des dernières commandes.

Chaque membre a sa propre politique de réservation. Lorsque vous réservez vous êtes prié de vous informer des conditions de cautionnement et d'annulation.

Dans la plupart des établissements, on parle au moins une langue étrangère. Les réservations sont indispensables.

Chacun des membres de l'Association publie une brochure individuelle qui vous sera adressée sur simple demande.

Pour tout renseignement complémentaire, s'adresser á:

Ireland's Blue Book,
8 Mount Street Crescent,
Dublin 2,
Ireland.

Tel:	+353-(0)1-6769914.
Fax:	+353-(0)1-6314990.
E-Mail:	mail@irelandsbluebook.com
Web Site:	www.irelandsbluebook.com

ROMANTICHE DIMORE DI CAMPAGNA E RISTORANTI DI CLASSE

Immersi nella rilassante bellezza dell'Irlanda verde, i ristoranti e le dimore di campagna, che fanno parte dell' IRELAND'S BLUE BOOK, offrono soluzioni esclusive adatte a tutti coloro che sono in cerca della tradizionale ospitalità degli irlandesi, oltre che della qualità eccellente della loro cucina.

In questo opuscolo – The Blue Book – sono elencati i ristoranti e le dimore di campagna che, per l'attenzione particolare riservata alle esigenze degli ospiti, sono vivamente consigliati dalle guide turistiche e dalla stampa internazionale.

Situate nelle vicinanze di rinomati campi da golf, centri di equitazione, distese di sabbia dorata, corsi d'acqua e laghi ricchi di trote e salmoni, queste dimore diventano un'ottima base dalla quale partire alla scoperta di un'antica e ben radicata cultura.

Scegliete tra le diverse soluzioni!
L'Associazione comprende quattro categorie:
1. Dimore di campagna con ristorante aperto anche ai non residenti.
2. Dimore di campagna con ristorante riservato ai soli ospiti resdienti.
3. Ristoranti con alloggio.
4. Ristoranti senza alloggio.

Potete scegliere di alloggiare in una grande residenza patrizia, nell' ambiente famigliare di una dimora di campagna oppure in un' accogliente locanda. Soluzioni, queste, diverse per carattere, stile e dimensioni, ma tutte con lo stesso livello di qualità, la stessa tradizionale e calorosa ospitalità. Il Blue Book contiene anche tre dei ristoranti più rinomati di Dublino, ideali per coloro che desiderano cenare in città.

Il prezzo indicato per il pernottamento e la prima colazione (B & B) è da intendersi, se non altrimenti indicato, per persona, in camera doppia con bagno/doccia.

Ogni proprietà applica proprie clausole di prenotazione. All'atto della prenotazione verificare pertanto le condizioni di deposito e cancellazione.

Il prezzo dei pasti è indicativo e gli orari si riferiscono alle prime e ultime ordinazioni.

A gestire sia i ristoranti che le dimore dell'ICHRA sono i proprietari stessi, sempre lieti di offrire informazioni e materiale illustrativo.

Nella maggior parte dei locali, si parlano una o più lingue straniere.
Vi ricordiamo che è indispensabile prenotare.

Correspondence & Enquiries:

Ireland's Blue Book,
8 Mount Street Crescent,
Dublin 2,
Ireland.
Tel: +353-(0)1-6769914.
Fax: +353-(0)1-6314990.
E-Mail: mail@irelandsbluebook.com
Web Site: www.irelandsbluebook.com

NASH'S MINERAL WATERS

18 75

www.nashswater.com

CASAS DE CAMPO Y RESTAURANTES IRLANDESES

Este 'BLUE BOOK' (Libro Azul) es una Asociación que comprende desde las casas de campo con más encanto a los más elegantes restaurantes de toda Irlanda. Los establecimientos que se describen en este folleto son dignos del visitante más exigente, en busca de altos niveles de hospitalidad tradicional, alojamiento y una cocina excelente dentro de la maravillosa tranquilidad de la Irlanda rural.

Todos los establecimientos de la Asociación están dirigidos personalmente por sus dueños. Muchos son famosos internacionalmente por su calidad y por lo tanto, figuran en guías turísticas y en revistas del mundo entero.

Si lo que desea es jugar al golf o pasear por paisajes pintorescos, escalar montañas, pescar en ríos o lagos, o caminar por extensas playas de arena fina, todas estas actividades podrá disfrutarlas en los alrededores de cualquiera de nuestras mansiones.

ELIJA SUS VACACIONES!
Los establecimientos están clasificados en cuatro categorias:
1. Mansiones señoriales cuyos restaurantes están abiertos a todo el mundo.
2. Mansiones señoriales cuyos restaurantes están reservados para sus huéspedes.
3. Restaurantes con alojamiento.
4. Restaurantes.

Podrá decidir entre alojarse en una mansion señorial, en una casa de campo en un ambiente familiar o en un acogedor restaurante con alojamiento. Todos estos establecimientos son muy originales, cualquiera de éstos le ofrece un sabor y ambiente diferente. Disfrutará de un caluro-o-so ambeinte, lleno de cordialidad y una cortesía de antaño. Encontrará un estupendo restaurante en los lugares más remotos de la isla. El Blue Book también contiene información sobre tres de los mejores restaurantes de Dublín para los que quieran cenar en la ciudad.

Los precios marcados son por persona en habitación doble con cuarto de baño/ducha, salvo que se indique lo contrario. El precio de almuerzos y cenas señalado, es un precio medio y el horario corresponde al primero y último servicio. Es imprescindible reservar con antelación. Cada establecimiento tiene su propio folleto, que le será enviado a vuelta de correo, una vez solicitado.

Cada miembro tiene su propio sistema de reservas. Cuando se haga una reserva, comprobar los tramites para los depositos y las cancelaciones.

Información / Preguntas

Ireland's Blue Book,
8 Mount Street Crescent,
Dublin 2,
Ireland.
Tel: +353-(0)1-6769914.
Fax: +353-(0)1-6314990.
E-Mail: mail@irelandsbluebook.com
Web Site: www.irelandsbluebook.com

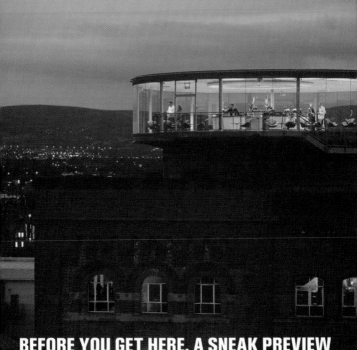

BEFORE YOU GET HERE, A SNEAK PREVIEW OF THE HIGH POINT OF YOUR TRIP

No, we're not about to spoil your trip by giving away too many secrets. Just consider this a little taste of what you'll discover for yourself at the Guinness Storehouse, Ireland's No.1 visitor attraction.

You'll find us slap-bang in the centre of Arthur Guinness's original 1759 brewery, still home to the legendary pint. See, hear, smell and feel this unique bond between city and brewery come to life as we take you on a surprising journey into the heart of the world's greatest beer.

Then when you're done exploring, enjoy a pint of Arthur's finest stout on us in Dublin's highest bar. And while you drink in the view, you'll understand why they say that you haven't experienced Dublin until you've discovered its vital ingredient...the Guinness Storehouse.

To find out more visit **www.guinness-storehouse.com** and book your tickets online.

Open daily 9.30am-5pm.
Late opening until 9pm during July & August.

DISCOVER THE VITAL INGREDIENT
www.guinness-storehouse.com

IRISCHE LANDHÄUSER UND RESTAURANTS

Hinter dem Namen "BLUE BOOK" verbirgt sich ein einzigartiger irischer Verband, der einige der bezauberndsten Landhotels und Restaurants des Landes vertritt.

Die Häuser, die Sie hier finden, bieten dem anspruchsvollen Besucher erstklassige Unterkunft, erlesene Küche und traditionelle irische Gastfreundschaft inmitten der anmutigen Schönheit und Ruhe des ländlichen Irland.

Jedes der genannten Anwesen wird vom Besitzer selbst geführt. In Reiseführern und Zeitschriften rund um die Welt werden Häuser des "Blue Book" – Verbandes immer wieder für ihren außergewöhnlichen Standard und ihr Ambiente gepriesen.

Möchten Sie Golf spielen? Berge erwandern, verträumte Flüsse und Seen zum Fischen entdecken, lange Spaziergänge an unberührten Sandstränden unternehmen oder einfach nur die großartige Landschaft genießen? Unsere Häuser liegen fast immer in der Nähe. . .

WÄHLEN SIE IHREN URLAUB

Die Mitglieder unserer Vereinigung gehören einer der folgenden vier Kategorien an:
1. Landhäuser mit Restaurant, die auch Nichthausgäste bewirten.
2. Landhäuser mit Restaurant nur für Hausgäste.
3. Restaurants mit Unterkunft.
4. Restaurants ohne Unterkunft.

Kein Haus gleicht dem anderen, jedes vermittelt eine eigene, einzigartige Atmosphäre. Doch ob sie Sich für das großzügige Herrenhaus, den freundlichen Landsitz oder das gemütliche Restaurant entscheiden – aufrichtige Gastfreundschaft und fast "altmodische" Höflichkeit in wohliger, entspannender Umgebung warten überall auf Sie. Selbst in den entlegensten Gegenden der grünen Insel werden Sie noch ein verstecktes Spitzenrestaurant entdecken. Wer gerne in Dublin essen gehen möchte, findet im Blue Book auch drei der besten Restaurants der Stadt.

In den Angaben der Dienstleistungen zu jedem Haus ist, falls nicht anders erwähnt, der Preis für Übernachtung und Frühstück (B & B) im Doppelzimmer mit Bad/dusche pro Person angegeben. Die Preise für das Abendessen verstehen sich als Durchschnittspreise, die angegebenen Zeiten für das Essen beziehen sich auf die früheste und letzte Bestellung. In den meisten Häusern wird mindestens eine kontinentaleuropäische Sprache gesprochen.

Jedes Mitglied hat seine eigenen Reservierungsgepflogenheiten. Wenn Sie buchen, fragen Sie bitte nach der jeweils erforderlichen Depositzahlung und den Stornierungbedingungen.

Alle Mitglieder des Verbandes haben eigene Broschüren, die sie Ihnen gerne zusenden.

Anfragen richten Sie bitte an:

Ireland's Blue Book,
8 Mount Street Crescent,
Dublin 2,
Ireland.
Tel: +353-(0)1-6769914.
Fax: +353-(0)1-6314990.
E-Mail: mail@irelandsbluebook.com
Web Site: www.irelandsbluebook.com

Where Special Moments Last Forever
Creators of Fine Jewellery

APPLEBY

DUBLIN

魅力的なカントリーハウス・ホテルとレストラン

「アイルランド・ブルーブック」には、アイルランドで指折りのカントリー・ハウス、城、レストランが加盟しています。静かで美しいアイルランドの自然のなかで、伝統的に名高いアイルランド流「おもてなし」が体験できる、宿泊施設、レストランをお探しの方に、最適の場をご紹介しています。

ゴルフや美しい景観、山でハイキング、川や湖で魚釣り、どこまでも続くビーチ。「ブルーブック」加盟の数多くのカントリーハウスが、こうしたリゾートにアクセス可能な場所にあります。目的に合わせて、ピッタリのカントリーハウスをお探しください。

どのような施設をお探しですか？
「ブルーブック」加盟店は、次の４つのカテゴリーに分かれています。
1．　レストラン付きカントリーハウス（レストランは宿泊者以外も利用可）
2．　食事付きカントリーハウス
3．　宿泊施設付きレストラン
4．　レストランのみ

豪奢なマナー・ハウス、親しみのあるカントリー・ハウス、宿泊もできる居心地のよいレストランなど、お好みに合わせてお選びください。同じ場所は二つとありません。どの場所も、独特の魅力を備えており、古式ゆかしい礼節を守りながらも、気のおけない、心のこもったおもてなしで皆様をお待ちしております。

「ブルーブック」はまた、ダブリン市内でお食事を望まれる方に向けて、ダブリンが誇る高級レストランを３店ご紹介しております。

サービス概要に記された**B&B**（ベッド・アンド・ブレックファスト：朝食付き宿泊）の料金は、特に明記していない限り、バス/シャワー付きダブルルーム２人使用１人あたりの価格です。シングル・ルームは追加料金がかかる場合があります。

ディナー料金は平均価格。ディナータイムは開店からラストオーダーまで。要予約。

予約の制度は場所により異なります。ご予約の際には、予約金およびキャンセル料の条件をお確かめください。全額をお支払いいただく場合もございます。また、ご自身の旅行傷害保険がキャンセル費用をサポートしているか否かもご確認ください。加盟店は各自パンフレットを用意しております。ご要望により送付いたします。

連絡／お問い合わせ

Ireland's Blue Book,
8 Mount Street Crescent,
Dublin 2,
Ireland.
電話番号： +353-(0)1-6769914
ファックス： +353-(0)1-6314990
電子メール： mail@irelandsbluebook.com
ホームページ： www.irelandsbluebook.com

THE PERFECT GIFT

IRELAND'S BLUE BOOK VOUCHERS

THE PERFECT GIFT

Ireland's Blue Book Vouchers
make the ideal present for Birthdays,
Anniversaries, Special Occasions or a
Corporate Incentive Presentation.

Vouchers are available in any denomination
of your choice (min. €100) and may be used
as payment or part payment for a stay or a meal
in any Blue Book House or Restaurant.

For further details please contact:

Ireland's Blue Book
8 Mount Street Crescent, Dublin 2, Ireland.

Tel: +353-(0)1-6769914 Fax: +353-(0)1-6314990
e-mail: mail@irelandsbluebook.com

MERRION

DUBLIN

The Merrion Hotel,
Upper Merrion Street,
Dublin 2, Ireland.
Tel: (353) 1 603 0600
Fax: (353) 1 603 0700
e-mail: info@merrionhotel.com
Web site: www.merrionhotel.com

Rates:	From	To
Single	€ 350	€ 420
Double	€ 370	€ 450
Suites	€ 650	€ 1100

Tax included, No service charge.

The Merrion, Dublin's most luxurious 5 star hotel is situated opposite Government Buildings in the city centre. Created from four Georgian Townhouses and a contemporary Garden Wing, The 142 bedrooms and suites are arranged around two 18th century style gardens. Stunningly restored interiors provide the perfect backdrop for one of Ireland's most impressive private art collections.

Guests have the choice of two restaurants including the 2 Michelin starred Restaurant Patrick Guilbaud, offering formal gourmet dining, and The Cellar Restaurant, which is dedicated to the finest seasonal Irish ingredients. Bars include The Cellar Bar set in the original wine vaults and the intimate cocktail bar, No 23.

Additional features include six private dining and conference rooms, underground car park and The Tethra Spa which boasts an 18m pool, gymnasium, steam room and luxurious private treatment rooms.

AHERNE'S SEAFOOD BAR

TOWNHOUSE AND SEAFOOD RESTAURANT

Open turf fires and the warmest of welcomes await you in this luxurious family run hotel (inn) in the historic walled port of Youghal (pronounced Yawl) at the mouth of the splendid River Blackwater.

Aherne's, in the Fitzgibbon family since 1923, has an internationally renowned restaurant specialising in the freshest of locally landed seafood. There's an old-world, traditional atmosphere in the bars where you can enjoy a pint with the locals and an array of tempting barfood. The restaurant specialises in locally caught seafood (lobster, prawns, turbot, salmon, monkfish, clams and mussels) and the menu changes daily, depending on what is fresh and available. Aherne's have twelve superior en suite guest bedrooms. All rooms are spacious, comfortable with tasteful decor and furnishings throughout. The modern conveniences of direct dial telephone, colour t.v., clothes press and hair dryer combine stylishly with the carefully chosen antiques to make it a most relaxing destination.

On our doorstep one can enjoy the best available in leisure activities to include golf, river and deep sea angling, equestrian facilities, sailing, or perhaps you might prefer to relax and stroll around the old town or on the hills, mountains and Blue Flag beaches nearby.

Fully equipped modern conference room with air conditioning suitable for meetings of up to 20 people.

Number of Bedrooms: 12 | Guesthouse ★ ★ ★ ★

Aherne's, 163 North Main Street, Youghal, Co. Cork.
Tel: 024-92424. Fax: 024-93633.
E. Mail: ahernes@eircom.net
Web Site: www.ahernes.com
Proprietors: The Fitzgibbon Family
Map Reference: 1.
Open: All year – except 5 days at Christmas.
Bed & Breakfast from €70-€105 pps.
Single from €105-€110.
Dinner 6.30 to 9.30pm – €45.
Bar Food Service available to 10pm daily.
Credit Cards: All.
Guide dogs welcome.

Reservations: Direct with Aherne's.
US Reps Tel Toll Free 800-323-5463,
GDS Code: LM.
or E. mail: usa@irelandsbluebook.com
How to find:
On the N25 (main Moscow to
Dingle Road!) Cork: 30 mins.
Rosslare: 2 hours.
Dublin: 3 hours.

YOUGHAL, CO. CORK.

1

ARDTARA
COUNTRY HOUSE AND RESTAURANT

Voted "Most Romantic Hotel of the Year" by the AA, Ardtara is a charming and elegant 19th century mansion, situated on the heart of Northern Ireland's unspoiled countryside.

Furnished throughout with antiques, you will find all the comfort, atmosphere and high standards of food, accommodation and service expected by only the most discerning visitors, all of which will be enhanced by the unusual warmth of the welcome.

Truly intimate, Ardtara offers eight luxury ensuite bedrooms, all individually styled with deluxe king size beds, original working fireplaces and panoramic views across the eight acres of grounds and beyond. The two AA Rosette restaurant, under the direction of Chef of the Year bronze medalist Martin Nelson complements the quality of accommodation.

Centrally located, Ardtara is just a short drive from some of Northern Ireland's finest attractions, such as The Antrim Coast and The Giant's Causeway and golf courses like world-famous Royal Portrush.

Number of Bedrooms: 8 | ★ ★ ★ ★ **Guesthouse**

Ardtara Country House, 8 Gorteade Road, Upperlands, Co. Derry BT46 5SA.
Tel: +44 (0) 28 796 44490.
Fax: +44 (0) 28 796 45080.
E. Mail: mary_breslin@ardtara.com
Web site: www.ardtara.com

Proprietor: Dr Alistair Hanna
General Manager: Mary Breslin

Map Reference: 2.
Closed 25 and 26 December.
Bed & full Irish breakfast from £60-£90 pps.
Single Supplement £20.
Dinner 7pm–9pm A la Carte. Restaurant non smoking.
Dinner available to non-residents by reservation.
Private Dining Room available if requested.

Credit Cards: Mastercard, Access, Visa, American Express. Meeting Rooms available.

Reservations:
Direct with house
In USA Tel Toll Free 800-323-5463,
or E. mail: usa@irelandsbluebook.com

How to find:
From Belfast, follow the M2 to the A6. After Castledawson take A29 to Maghera. Follow B75 to Kilrea until you come to Upperlands.

UPPERLANDS, CO. DERRY.

BALLYLICKEY MANOR HOUSE
COUNTRY HOUSE AND RESTAURANT

Ballylickey, built over 300 years ago as a shooting lodge for Lord Kenmare, has been home for the French Irish Graves family for four generations.

On the boundary of Cork and Kerry amidst ten acres of award winning flower gardens and parkland surrounded by mountains and moorland it enjoys a stunning romantic setting overlooking Bantry Bay.

There is an aura of quiet luxury about the Manor with its drawing rooms, dining rooms, breakfast room and seven sumptuous suites. Across the gardens, just out of sight, are the swimming pool and a cluster of comfortable Cottages which offer a choice of suites, apartments and bedroom bathroom accommodation.

Ballylickey is an ideal centre from which to tour the beautiful south west of Ireland, that also offers private trout and salmon fishing in the Park, a heated outdoor swimming pool, two golf courses and riding nearby.

Ballylickey is recommended by the leading European Hotel and Restaurant guides.

Number of Bedrooms: 4 | Number of Suites: 8

Ballylickey Manor House,
Ballylickey, Bantry, Co. Cork.
Tel: 027-50071. Fax: 027-50124.
E. Mail: ballymh@eircom.net
Web site: ballylickeymanorhouse.com
Proprietors: Christiane & George Graves
Map Reference: 3.
Open: March – November.
Bed and Breakfast from €80-€135 pps, low season; from €80-€171 pps, high season.
Price include Tax and Service.
Dinner: From €47 per person.
Half board and special spring and autumn rates on request.

Ground floor bedrooms in Cottages.
All major Credit Cards accepted.
French spoken.

Reservations:
Call us direct, within Ireland 027-50071
From UK and Europe 00-353-27-50071
From USA 0-11-353-27-50071
US Reps Tel Toll Free 800-323-5463
or E. mail: usa@irelandsbluebook.com

How to find:
On main road N71
between Bantry and
Glengariff/ Kenmare Road.

BANTRY, CO. CORK.

3

BALLYMALOE HOUSE

COUNTRY HOUSE AND RESTAURANT

Ballymaloe House is a large family farmhouse, situated on a 400 acre farm, 20 miles east of Cork city. The house is two miles from the coast, near the small fishing village of Ballycotton and many small sandy coves and beaches. The Knockmealdown and Comeragh Mountains are about one hour's drive away. There are also several historic houses and gardens open to the public within a short distance.

Amenities include a small golf course on premises, large golf course (international standard) 12 miles. Sea and river fishing arranged 5-20 miles. Riding arranged 10 miles. Outdoor heated pool (summer use). Direct dialling from bedrooms. Babysitting available. Outdoor children's play area. Tennis court. Ground floor rooms in courtyard.

Members of the family also run an excellent craft and specialist kitchenware shop on the premises, the Ballymaloe Cookery School in Shanagarry and the restaurant in the Crawford Art Gallery in Cork City.

The food is largely produced on the home farm and has won high recommendation in various guides.

Number of Bedrooms: 34

Ballymaloe House,
Shanagarry, Midleton, Co. Cork.
Tel: 021-4652531. Fax: 021-4652021.
E. Mail: res@ballymaloe.ie
Web site: www.ballymaloe.ie

Proprietors: Allen Family.
Map Reference: 4.
Closed: 24, 25, 26 December.
Bed & Breakfast pps €97.50-€122.50 low season; €107.50-€142.50 high season.
Single Supplement €25.
Service charge optional.
Dinner €55.50 from 7.00–9.30pm.
All major credit cards accepted.

Children welcome.

Reservations:
US Reps Tel Toll Free: 800-323-5463
or E. mail: usa@irelandsbluebook.com

How to find:
From Cork take N25 east. Then take the R630 and R631. We are 2 miles beyond Cloyne on the Ballycotton road. From Waterford take the N25 west to Castlemartyr. Follow signs to Ballymaloe. Take care in Ladysbridge.

MIDLETON, CO. CORK.

BARBERSTOWN CASTLE

CASTLE AND COUNTRY HOUSE

Barberstown Castle is an internationally known, historic Country House Hotel. Built in the 13th century, the Castle is situated only 30 minutes drive from both Dublin Airport and the City Centre, thus making it an ideal first or last visit on your Country House tour of Ireland.

The perfect Castle to stay while visiting Dublin city. The Restaurant at Barberstown is renowned for its creative food and has consistently received the RAC Restaurant award and also Rosettes from the AA.

Each of the en suite bedrooms have been decorated in an individual style and dedicated to the ordinary and extraordinary people who have lived within its walls over the past seven hundred years.

Four days unforgettable golfing can be arranged at the K-Club (Ryder Cup 2006) on the original Arnold Palmer Course or the new Parkland Links, along with Carton, hosting both the Mark O'Meara and Colin Montgomery Courses – this Holiday is a golfer's dream.

Horse riding, hunting, fishing and shooting can all be arranged through the Castle.

For the less active – relax in an atmosphere of pure calm and tranquillity, enjoying open log fires, good food and convivial company.

Number of Bedrooms: 22

Barberstown Castle, Straffan, Co. Kildare.
Tel: 01-628 8157.
Fax: 01-627 7027.
I.T.B./AA/RAC
E. Mail: castleir@iol.ie
Web site: www.barberstowncastle.ie
Proprietor: Ken Healy.
Manager: Richard Millea.

Map Reference: 5.
Open: All year except three days at Christmas.
Bed and Breakfast €95pps-€110 pps.
€30 singular room supplement.
Dinner 7.30 to 9.30pm - Open for Lunch.
A la Carte & Tasting Menu.

Credit Cards: Visa/Access/Amex/Diners.

Reservations:
US Reps Tel Toll Free 800-323-5463,
or E. mail: usa@irelandsbluebook.com
or Direct with the Castle.

How to find:
Travelling west on N4 take the
turn for Straffan at Maynooth.
Travelling South on N7 take
the turn for Straffan at Kill.

BARBERSTOWN CASTLE,
STRAFFAN, CO. KILDARE.

5

BELLE ISLE CASTLE

COUNTRY HOUSE

Belle Isle is situated on one of the eleven islands that are owned by the Estate on Upper Lough Erne. A bridge connects the island to the mainland. There are 470 acres in this magical Estate which includes a 90 cow dairy herd. The original Castle was built in 1680 and further extended in 1850. It has had three owners during its noted history which includes the present owner, the Duke of Abercorn.

The Castle has been kept in its original layout so that guests will enjoy the romance of a bygone era. Expect an authentic Country House atmosphere without the frills of modern restorations. Antique furniture and paintings by Victorian masters are all offset beautifully by the dramatic colour scheme created by esteemed international interior designer, David Hicks. The collection also includes some striking Russian paintings from St. Petersburg.

On arrival guests will be welcomed by Charles and Fiona Plunket whose objective is to make all their visitors welcome and ensure that their stay will be a memorable one. Northern Ireland is noted for its fine food and Belle Isle's cuisine lives up to this reputation.

On the estate there is a tennis court, croquet lawn and boats for hire. A wooden cruiser is also available for parties up to 14 to tour the Lough. The region has an abundance of National Trust properties, such as Florence Court, Castle Coole and the Crom Estate. Amongst the many amenities to be enjoyed in the area are; three excellent golf courses within a half hour's drive and superb game fishing on Lough Melvin and the river Mourne.

The Belle Isle School of Cookery opened in the autumn of 2003 and further details can be obtained from **www.irishcookeryschool.com**

Number of Bedrooms: 8 | **Specialist Accommodation: historic house**

Belle Isle Estate, Lisbellaw, Co. Fermanagh.
N. Ireland BT94 5HG.
Tel: +44 (0)28 66387231.
Fax: +44 (0)28 66387261.
E. Mail: accommodation@belleisle-estate.com
Web site: www.belleislecastle.com

Proprietor: Duke of Abercorn KG
Land Agent: Charles Plunket

Map Reference: 6.
Open: All year.
B&B: Stg £50-70 pps.
Minimum stay: 2 bedrooms for 2 nights.
Single supplement: Stg £15.
Dinner at 8.30pm. Stg £25.

All major credit cards accepted.
Ideal for private parties/small weddings.

Reservations:
Direct with the house.
US Reps Tel Toll Free 800-323-5463,
or E mail: usa@irelandsbluebook.com

How to find:
From Belfast take the A4 to Enniskillen. Follow signs to Carry Bridge and signposted thereafter. From Dublin take N3 and Carry bridge thereafter.

LISBELLAW, CO. FERMANGH

BLAIRS COVE HOUSE

RESTAURANT AND ACCOMMODATION

In this 250 year old Georgian country house standing at the head of Dunmanus Bay, everything revolves around the courtyard. It is finely restored with cobbled paths, shrubs and flowers. The old stone outbuildings house three beautiful suites and the restaurant with its magnificent dining room converted from the old stableblock. A perfect blending of the old and new!

Blairs Cove House is well known through its restaurant which opened in 1981 and famous for its buffet style starters and great, open, wood fired grill. It is recommended by all the major food guides.

What the critics say:

> *"Blairs Cove Restaurant has one of the most beautiful settings of any restaurant"* – **Irish Times**

> *"Unter den guten Lokalen im Suedwesten das Schoenste und unter den schoenen Lokalen das Beste"* – **Feinschmecker**

> *"A jewel in the culinary crown of West Cork"* – **The Tribune**

Cork Airport 1 hour 30 minutes.
Four golf courses, horseriding, sailing and sandy beaches nearby.
Winner of the Georgina Campbell's 'Most atmospheric restaurant award' 2003.

Number of Bedrooms: 3 courtyard suites, 1 cottage in the grounds

Blairs Cove House, Durrus near Bantry, Co. Cork.
Tel: 027-61127. Fax: 027-61487.
E. Mail: blairscove@eircom.net

Proprietors: Philippe & Sabine De Mey
Map Reference: 7.

Restaurant:
Open 19 March to 31 October.
Dinner only from 7.30pm - 9.30pm.
Table d'hôte €50
Closed Sundays and Mondays.

Accommodation:
Open March to November.
Bed & Breakfast €85-€100. Single supplement €30. Self catering cottage available.

No service charge. Major credit cards accepted. German, French and Dutch spoken.

Reservations:
Call us direct: From UK 00 353 27 61127
From USA 011 353 27 61127
US Reps Tel Toll Free: 800-323-5463,
or E mail: usa@irelandsbluebook.com.

How to find:
Coming from Durrus follow the R591 to Goleen/Barleycove, 1.5 miles outside the village you'll find a blue gate on the right-hand side.

DUNMANUS BAY, CO. CORK.

BUSHMILLS INN

HOTEL AND RESTAURANT

In the village that is home to the world's oldest distillery, between the Giant's Causeway and Royal Portrush Golf Club, this "living museum of Ulster Hospitality" has been outstandingly successful in recreating its origins as an old Coaching Inn and Mill House.

Intriguing fireplaces, oil lamps, nooks, crannies and even a secret room set the tone. In the bar, still lit by gas light, try a glass of Bushmills malt from the hotels private cask or relax in a rocking chair in front of the gentle glow of a turf fire in the 'old kitchen'. The award winning restaurant, blending 'new Irish' cuisine with finest North Antrim produce, overlooks the garden courtyard and contrasts intimate 'snugs' with white washed walls and warm mellow brick with well aged timbers.

Take the grand staircase to the Gallery, the gateway to the bedrooms, where the magnificence of the Causeway Coast is captured in oils and water colours. The spacious Mill House bedrooms, on the banks of the River Bush, have their own sitting area and small dressing room while the smaller Coaching Inn rooms, mostly overlook the village.

Golf Hotel of the Year 2003 (Irish Golf Tour Operators Association).

You're welcome.

Number of Bedrooms: 32 | Historic Building

The Bushmills Inn, 9 Dunluce Road, Bushmills, Co Antrim BT57 8QG
Tel: +44 (0)28 2073 3000
Fax: +44 (0)28 2073 2048
E. Mail: mail@bushmillsinn.com
Web site: www.bushmillsinn.com
Proprietor: Roy Bolton
Managers: Alan Dunlop & Stella Minogue
Map Reference 8.
Open all year, 7 days a week.
B&B Mill House from: Stg£64-£99 pps
B&B Coaching Inn from: Stg£44-£49 pps
All bedrooms no smoking.
Restaurant open all day. Dinner from 7.00 to 9.30pm - Stg£28. Meeting Rooms, Helipad.
Credit Cards: Visa, MasterCard.

Reservations:
Web, Tel, Fax, E-mail or
US reps Toll Free 800-323-5463
or E mail: usa@irelandsbluebook.com

How to find:
(2 miles from Giant's Causeway)
on the A2 (Antrim Coast Road)
in the village of Bushmills
as you cross the River Bush.

BUSHMILLS, CO. ANTRIM

CARAGH LODGE

COUNTRY HOUSE AND RESTAURANT

One mile from the famous "Ring of Kerry", in an award-winning garden of Azaleas, Camelias and Magnolias, you will find Caragh Lodge. A mid Victorian house, Caragh Lodge was originally built as a fishing lodge and is on the shores of Caragh Lake, looking towards the McGillicuddy Reeks (Ireland's highest mountain).

In addition to salmon and trout fishing, in the summer, the lake is ideal for boating and swimming. Being no more than a short drive from Ballybunion (1½ hrs.), Waterville (45 mins.), Killarney (30 mins.), Beaufort (20 mins.) and Tralee (45 mins.), and only 10 minutes from Dooks Golf Club, Caragh Lodge is the ideal centre for golfing holidays. Horseriding and miles of unspoilt sandy beaches are within a 10 minute drive.

The Proprietor, Mary Gaunt, personally supervises the kitchen and reservations for dinner are advisable. Seafood, Wild Salmon and Kerry Lamb feature strongly on the menu. In keeping with its surroundings the Lodge is furnished throughout with antiques and the 15 comfortable bedrooms are centrally heated and have en suite facilities.

RAC Small Hotel of the Year 1996. RAC Blue Ribbon Award 1998, RAC Gold Ribbon Award 1999, 2000, 2001, 2002, 2003.

Johansens Country Houses and Small Hotels Award for Excellence 1999.

Number of Bedrooms: 15 | Guesthouse ★ ★ ★ ★

**Caragh Lodge, Caragh Lake,
Killorglin, Co. Kerry.**
Tel: 066-9769115. Fax: 066-9769316.
E. Mail: caraghl@iol.ie
Web site: www.caraghlodge.com
Proprietor: Mary Gaunt.

Map Reference: 9.
Open: 22 April – 17 October.
Bed and Breakfast: €90-€115 pps.
Single Room: €130. 1 Suite: €167.50 pps.
Dinner open to non-residents, 7.00pm to
8.30pm, á la Carte. No Service Charge.
Credit Cards:
Visa/Access/Mastercard/Amex/Diners Club.

Reservations:
Direct with us.
US Reps Tel. Toll Free: 800-323-5463
or E. mail: usa@irelandsbluebook.com.
How to find:
From Killorglin on N70 towards
Glenbeigh, take second road
signposted "Caragh Lodge 1 mile".
At lake turn left, the lodge is
on your right.

CARAGH LAKE, CO. KERRY.

9

CASHEL HOUSE HOTEL
COUNTRY HOUSE AND RESTAURANT

Cashel House Hotel, formerly one of Connemara's most gracious homes, stands at the head of Cashel Bay, withdrawn and quietly secluded, in a 40 acre estate of flowering shrubs and woodland walks.

In 1968 it was opened as an hotel by skilled hoteliers, Dermot and Kay McEvilly, who have since then been joined by their family in running the hotel which has gained for itself an international reputation for good food and comfort in a quiet, relaxing atmosphere. In 1969 the late General and Madame DeGaulle spent two weeks of their Irish holiday there. Beaches, golf, salmon and sea-trout fishing are available in the vicinity. The hotel has its own hard tennis court, tiny private beach. All rooms have direct dial telephones, T.V. and full central heating.

All good guides recommend Cashel House. Suitable for longer restful stays.

RAC Blue Ribbon Award 1992, '93, '94, '95, '96, '97 and '98. Gold Ribbon in 1999, 2000, 2001 and 2002.

Number of Bedrooms: 17 | Number of Suites: 13 | Hotel ★ ★ ★ ★

Cashel House Hotel, Cashel, Co. Galway.
Tel: 095-31001.
Fax: 095-31077.
E. Mail: info@cashel-house-hotel.com
Web site: www.cashel-house-hotel.com
Proprietors: McEvilly family.
Map Reference: 10.
Open: 4 February – 10 January.
Bed and Breakfast from €80-€110 low season; €120-€150) high season.
12.5% Service charge. Dinner €43-€46.
Credit Cards: American Express/Visa/
MasterCard/Eurocard
Not suitable for children under 5.

Irish, French and German Spoken.
Dogs welcome.

Reservations:
US Reps Tel Toll Free: 800-323-5463,
or E mail: usa@irelandsbluebook.com
or direct with the House.

How to find:
South off N59 (Galway
Clifden Road).
1 mile west of Recess,
turn left.

CASHEL, CO. GALWAY.

CASTLE DURROW

COUNTRY HOUSE AND RESTAURANT

Shelly and Peter have filled this stunning house with so much informal warmth that it feels more family home than Hotel. This lovingly restored 300 year old Mansion looks over its beautiful terraced gardens to the South and the River Erkina to the North. This contemporary Country House Hotel welcomes you from the minute you arrive and engulfs you with its eclectic mix of furniture and style. Set in the middle of Ireland, a short distance from busy, cultural Kilkenny, most of Ireland is within easy reach.

Built in 1716 and extended in the early eighteen hundreds to incorporate new fashions and extended living accommodation fit for a Viscount, Castle Durrow now boasts large and bright reception areas, dining rooms and bedrooms. All have been given their own modern identity without losing their original architectural features.

Shelly and Peter have brought their many years' restaurant experience to the Castle. Lots of the ingredients for the fabulous food are supplied by the Castle's own organic kitchen garden along with locally sourced produce.

River, parkland, forest walks and cycling are in abundance. Golf easily arranged in any of four nearby courses. Seasonal fishing on the Estate, horse riding and tennis in the grounds and croquet or boules on the lawn provides the perfect getaway.

Number of Bedrooms: 26

Castle Durrow, Durrow, Co. Laois.
Tel: +353 (0) 502 36555.
Fax: +353 (0) 502 36559.
E. Mail: info@castledurrow.com
Website: www.castledurrow.com
Proprietor: The Stokes Family

Map Reference: 11.
Open all year except three days at Christmas and New Year's Eve.
Restaurant open Wednesday to Sunday.
Closed: January 15th (1 week).
Bed & Breakfast from €90 pps.
Single and group rates available on request.
Dinner 4 course Table D'hote €45.
Special Dinner, Bed & Breakfast rates.

Conferences. Weddings up to 170 guests. Gift vouchers available. House parties (must take all rooms).
Reservations:
Direct with Castle Durrow by telephone or E. mail.
In USA tel: Toll Free 800-323-5463
or E. mail: usa@irelandsbluebook.com
How to find:
On main Dublin–Cork N8,
in the centre of Durrow
village.

DURROW, CO. LAOIS

11

CHAPTER ONE RESTAURANT

RESTAURANT

Chapter One Restaurant is located in the heart of Dublin on the northside of Parnell Square. As a Georgian basement, and former home of John Jameson, it retains authentic granite walls and sash windows but has been carefully and stylishly renovated to introduce a wonderfully sumptuous and comfortable restaurant.

The reception area boasts a wonderfully carved Oyster Counter accompanied by some of the finest champagnes. Private dining rooms are available in the restaurant and the beautifully ornate Gallery of Writers is a wonderful banqueting room.

It is one of Dublin's leading restaurants having recently won the Evian/Food and Wine Best Service award for 2003. The front of house team are warm and friendly while retaining a high level of efficiency and professionalism. The food at Chapter One is a delicate blend of old style with innovative twists which makes for a wonderfully creative menu. The emphasis is on organic and seasonal produce to produce the best possible dining experience for the customer. It is Dublin's premier pre-theatre dining venue.

Ross Lewis and Martin Corbett, Chapter One's co-proprietors, have continued to strive for excellence and this effort is manifest throughout the restaurant. A rare treat awaits you.

Chapter One Restaurant
18/19 Parnell Square, Dublin 1.
Tel: 01-873 2266.
Fax: 01-873 2330.
E. Mail: info@chapteronerestaurant.com
Proprietors: Ross Lewis and Martin Corbett

Map Reference: 12.
Opening hours: Tuesday–Friday 12.30–2.30;
Tuesday–Saturday 6.00–11.00.
Annual Holidays: Christmas – two weeks;
August – two weeks.
Private Dining:
The Jameson Room: 14 people.
The Vault Room: 20 people.

Reservations: Direct with the restaurant.
US Reps Tel Toll Free: 800-323-5463
or E. mail: usa@irelandsbluebook.com
How to find:
Centre of Dublin – Parnell Square is at the top of O'Connell Street.

PARNELL SQUARE, DUBLIN.

COOPERSHILL HOUSE

COUNTRY HOUSE

Coopershill is a fine example of a Georgian family mansion. Home to 7 generations of the O'Hara family since it was built in 1774, it combines the spaciousness and elegance of an earlier age with the comfort and amenities of today. Most of the bedrooms have four poster or canopy beds and all have private bathrooms. The rooms retain their original regal dimensions and are furnished in keeping with the period of the house.

Candle-lit dinners, wide choice of wines, open log fires and personal attention from the owners all help to create the atmosphere and hospitality that is special to Coopershill.

Standing at the centre of a 500 acre estate of deer farm and woodland, separation from the outside world seems complete. There are many delightful walks and wildlife is abundant and undisturbed.

Boating and fishing are available nearby and we have an all-weather Tennis Court and Croquet. Championship golf courses and fine beaches are within an hour's drive along with the spectacular mountains and lakes of Yeats' country.

Number of Bedrooms: 8 | **Specialist Accommodation Historic House**

Coopershill House, Riverstown, Co. Sligo.
Tel: 071-9165108.   Fax: 071-9165466.
E. Mail: ohara@coopershill.com
web site: www.coopershill.com
Proprietors: Brian & Lindy O'Hara
Map Reference: 13.
Open: 1 April – 1 November.
Bed and Breakfast from €85-€93 low
season; €96-€109 high season.
Single Supplement €19.
Dinner at 8.30pm €42-€48.
No service charge.
Special 3 and 6 day breaks.
All major Credit Cards accepted.
Dogs allowed, but not in the house.

Reservations: Direct with the house:
Tel: +353-7191-65108
Fax: +353-7191-65466
US Reps Tel Toll Free: 800-323-5463
or E. mail: usa@irelandsbluebook.com
How to find:
Signed from Drumfin Crossroads,
11 miles south-east of Sligo
on route N4 to Dublin.
Extra information:
Out of season house
parties by arrangement.

RIVERSTOWN, CO. SLIGO.

13

CROMLEACH LODGE

COUNTRY HOUSE & RESTAURANT

"Irish Hotel of the Year 1999" – Cromleach Lodge is set in the quiet hills above Lough Arrow, with the pre-historic Carrowkeel Cairns meeting the ever-changing sky beyond – a spectacular vista of unspoiled mountain, lake and valley.

All rooms/mini-suites are exceptionally spacious and well appointed, each is individually decorated and each enjoys the breathtaking panorama of south Sligo. The atmosphere is warm and relaxed with Irish liqueur and fresh fruit in your room, newspapers with breakfast and the scent of fresh flowers all around.

But Cromleach Lodge's piece de resistance is its Restaurant, where dishes created by Moira – "Irish Chef of the Year 2000" and her team are a gastronomic delight. Highly acclaimed in all leading guides, Cromleach Lodge has won many awards, including "Best Connacht Restaurant 2003". The perfect haven from which to explore the natural beauty of Yeats Country and the North West with carefully mapped scenic drives and nature walks through fields and woodlands to breathe the freshest air and absorb the tranquil silence in this paradise of nature. Golf at Rosses Point, Enniscrone or Murvagh also lake, river or sea fishing.

Number of Bedrooms: 10 Including Superior Rooms | Hotel ★ ★ ★ ★

**Cromleach Lodge, Castlebaldwin,
Via Boyle, Co. Sligo.**
Tel: 071-9165155. Fax: 071-9165455.
E. Mail: info@cromleach.com
Web site: www.cromleach.com
Proprietors: Christy & Moira Tighe
Map Reference: 14.
Open: 1 February – 2 November.
Bed and Breakfast from €120-€150 low season; €158-€188 high season.
Single occupancy €45 extra.
Special 2 and 3 day breaks.
Dinner €55 (private dining available).
All major credit cards accepted.
Dogs welcome.

Dining rooms non-smoking.
Executive meeting room.
Helipad - GPS: N 54.05.22 W 08.19.04
Reservations:
US Reps Tel Toll Free: 800-323-5463,
or E mail: usa@irelandsbluebook.com
or direct with hotel
How to find:
Signposted from
Castlebaldwin on the N4
(8 miles west of Boyle and
17 miles east of Sligo).

CASTLEBALDWIN, CO. SLIGO.

CURRAREVAGH HOUSE

COUNTRY HOUSE

Old fashioned (in the best sense of the word), Currarevagh is a Victorian country manor romantically situated on the shores of Lough Corrib in 150 acres of private woodland. Built by the present owner's ancestors in 1842, it is still run more along the lines of a private country house rather than as an hotel and while extremely comfortable, it is neither "luxurious" nor pretentious. Consequently, the tranquil informality lends itself to those seeking a relaxing few days. Lough Corrib is famous for its wild brown trout fishing and Ghillies (guides) can be arranged at current rates. There is an 18 hole golf course in Oughterard and five other courses within an hours drive.

Having all Connemara (including the Aran Islands and The Burren) within easy reach for touring, and having our own boats, our own tennis court and wild country walks nearby, Currarevagh is the ideal place for that longer break, especially as the better known Food Guides highly recommend its classically simple menus based on local produce. (Dinner for non-residents by advance booking only).

"It is difficult to think of a more romantic place than this 19th century mansion on the shore of Lough Corrib. It is renowned for its exquisite evening meals and quality accommodation" – Lonely Planet Guide 2003.

Number of Bedrooms: 15 | Guesthouse   ★ ★ ★ ★

Currarevagh House, Oughterard, Connemara, Co. Galway.
Tel: 091-552312/091-552313.
Fax: 091-552731.
E. Mail: mail@currarevagh.com
Web site: www.currarevagh.com
Proprietors: Harry, June and Henry Hodgson.
Map Reference: 15.
Open: 1 April to 21 October (approx).
Bed and Breakfast from €75-€95 low season; €80-€105 high season.
Single Supplement €30.
Dinner €37.50. 10% service charge.
Credit Cards: Visa, Mastercard, Laser. French spoken.
Cancellation Policy: 1 to 31 May – 3 weeks notice. Rest of season – 7 days notice.

Reservations: Direct with house.
US Reps Tel Toll Free: 800-323-5463.
How to find: Take the N59 (Galway/ Clifden) road to Oughterard. Turn right in village square and follow the Glann road for 4 miles (6km).
Extra information: 3-6 day half board rate €112 pp per day. Weekly half board rate €710 pp per week. Out of season house parties of 10 or more guests welcome (excluding Christmas and New Year).

OUGHTERARD, CONNEMARA, CO. GALWAY.

DOYLE'S

SEAFOOD RESTAURANT AND TOWNHOUSE

Doyles Seafood Restaurant is famous the world over for seafood, fresh from the ocean and is synonymous with Dingle. Originally a small shop and pub built in 1790. The award winning restaurant with its flagstone floors, stone walls, cosy arrangement of tables, sugan chairs and original cast Iron Range. Locally caught seafood is the main attraction with lobster selected from a tank in the bar a speciality. There are however concessions to non-seafood eaters, Chicken, Steaks, Duck, Kerry Lamb, guinness stew as well as vegetable paella etc. Puddings are scrumptious and traditional. There is also a plated selection of farmhouse cheeses from the Munster Area. The Restaurant is fully air conditioned and offers a non smoking area.

The townhouse has the most delightful rooms in Dingle, and has recently been totally refurbished. 8 spacious bedrooms with full bathrooms en suite are decorated in a most comfortable traditional style with antique furnishings and 21st century amenities such as satellite tv. phone, trouser press/iron, tea/coffee facilities etc. The drawing room is decorated in a Victorian setting and is very welcoming with its open fire, pine floors and soft furnishings.

RAC, AA, Michelin recommended, Tourist Board "Award of Excellence", Egon Roonay "Seafood Dish of the Year". "Les Routier" Restaurant of the year 2002.

Number of Bedrooms: 8 | **Guesthouse ★ ★ ★**

Doyle's Seafood Bar & Townhouse,
John Street, Dingle, Co. Kerry.
Tel: 066 9151174 Fax: 066 9151816.
Email: cdoyles@iol.ie
www.doylesofdingle.com

Proprietors: Sean & Charlotte Cluskey.

Map Reference: 16.
Open: Mid February-Mid November.
Bed and Breakfast from €59-€69 low
season; €85-€92 high season.
Single room from €104-€170.
Dinner approx €45 from 6pm.
All major credit cards.
Restaurant closed Sunday.
We do not accept dogs.

Reservations:
US Reps Tel Toll Free: 800-323-5463,
E mail: usa@irelandsbluebook.com, your
travel agent or Direct with house.

How to find:
In heart of Dingle Town off the Mall

DINGLE, CO. KERRY

16

COUNTRY HOUSE HOTEL AND RESTAURANT

This captivating 1830's Georgian manor hides amid 300 acres of tranquil parklands on the idyllic Hook Peninsula, just 15 minutes east of Waterford City. A chic yet delightfully informal ambience permeates Dunbrody, where guests have the opportunity to experience sheer indulgence coupled with our tradition of courteous attentive service. Personal attention to detail is evident throughout - fresh flowers, crackling log and turf fires in period fireplaces, cosy bar and a choice of spacious, elegantly appointed bedrooms all equipped with DVDs.

Enjoy one of our famous late breakfasts (served till Noon every day). With a host of awards and recommendations, the Dunbrody Experience is a must for those who wish to sample the best of Irish cuisine in the most relaxing of great Irish houses.

Dunbrody Cookery School also offers a choice of residential courses for Food Lovers of all abilities (See our advert).

"I would rate Kevin as one of Ireland's best chefs" – **Condé Nast Traveller**
"This historic country retreat is both stylish and pleasantly informal" – **Fodor's Guide**

Grand Award Winner Andrew Harper's Hideaway Report 2002.

Number of Bedrooms: 22 Including Suites and Junior Suites | **Hotel ★ ★ ★ ★**

Dunbrody Country House Hotel, Arthurstown, (Nr. Waterford), Co. Wexford.
Tel: +353 (0)51-389600.
Fax: +353 (0)51-389601.
E. Mail: dunbrody@indigo.ie
Web Site: www.dunbrodyhouse.com
Proprietors: Kevin & Catherine Dundon.
Map Reference: 17.
Open all year except Christmas 20-27 Dec.
Bed and Breakfast pps €100-€155 low season; €120-€200 high season.
Single supplement €25.
Dinner from €55. Table d'Hote Menu.
Service Charge at your own discretion.
All major credit cards accepted.
Wheelchair facilities, French/German spoken.
Weekend packages from €199 pps 2BB1D.

Packages also available for Bank Holiday weekends and New Year.
Book online: www.dunbrodyhouse.com
Reservations: Direct with Dunbrody. US Reps Tel. Toll Free: 800-323-5463. GDS Code: Apollo/Galileo/Amadeus/Sabre /Worldspan.
How to find: M11/ N11 from Dublin to Wexford. R733 from Wexford to Arthurstown. 100 miles from Dublin or Cork. 40 miles from Rosslare port. N25 from Cork to Waterford and Pasage East car ferry to Arthurstown.

ARTHURSTOWN, CO. WEXFORD.

ENNISCOE HOUSE

COUNTRY HOUSE

Enniscoe House is listed as a heritage house of Ireland, and has passed to the present owner by inheritance. The family portraits, antique furniture, open fires, good food and wine, and a warm welcome, all contribute to the pleasant and relaxed atmosphere.

The house is situated on the shores of Lough Conn, with attractive views of the lake across the parkland. The old walled garden is being restored, and another garden produces organically grown vegetables. One farmyard now houses a small agricultural museum and the genealogy centre that researches names and families of Mayo origin.

There is brown trout fishing on Lough Conn, other trout and salmon fishing nearby. The fishery manager can make all arrangements for boats, gillies, tuition, and hire of equipment.

There are three golf courses within easy reach, and riding stables in the area. Enniscoe is a good centre for exploring north Mayo, Achill to the south, and Sligo to the north.

Number of Bedrooms: 6 | Specialist Accommodation Historic House

Enniscoe House, Castlehill,
Nr. Crossmolina, Ballina, Co. Mayo.
Tel: 096-31112. Fax: 096-31773,
E. Mail: mail@enniscoe.com
Web site: www.enniscoe.com
Proprietors: Susan Kellett & D.J. Kellett.
Map Reference: 18.
Open: 1 April – 31 October.
Bed and Breakfast €80-€86 low season;
€86-€98 high season.
Dinner €40 at 8.00pm.
Single Supplement: €20.
No service charge.
Credit Cards: Visa/Access/Amex.
Dogs welcome.

Reservations:
US Reps Tel. Toll Free: 800-323-5463,
E mail: usa@irelandsbluebook.com, your
travel agent or direct with the House.
How to find:
Enniscoe is two miles south of Crossmolina
on the R315 to Pontoon and Castlebar. It is
12 miles from Ballina.

CROSSMOLINA, CO. MAYO.

St. Ernans House Hotel

COUNTRY HOUSE AND RESTAURANT

Quietly situated on a wooded tidal island, connected to the mainland by a causeway, St. Ernans offers the perfect respite from the hectic pace of everyday life.

There is a unique warmth and sense of serenity at St. Ernans. It recaptures the charm of the past-quietude in a relaxing friendly atmosphere.

The house, built in 1826 by John Hamilton, a nephew of the Duke of Wellington has 10 rooms each with private bath or shower and telephone. Most have stunning views of the sea and countryside. The diningroom is one of country elegance where the cuisine is based on fresh local produce.

From this perfectly situated house the countryside may be explored. There are several excellent golf courses nearby. Horseriding, fishing and bicycle hire are also available locally.

St. Ernans offers the perfect escape from the pressures of modern life to the finest traditions of Irish Country House hospitality.

Number of Bedrooms: 8 | Number of Suites: 2 | Hotel ★ ★ ★ ★

St. Ernans House Hotel, Donegal, Co. Donegal.
Tel: 074-9721065. Fax: 074-9722098.
E. Mail info@sainternans.com
Web site: www.sainternans.com

Proprietors: Brian & Carmel O'Dowd
Map Reference: 19.
Open: Mid April – End October.
Bed and Breakfast from €130-€160 pps low season; €140-€175 pps high season.
Suites Available: €200-€220 pps.
Dinner from €42. No service charge.
Credit Cards: Access/Visa/ Mastercard.
Children under six not catered for.

Reservations:
Direct with House,
Online reservations www.sainternans.com
E. mail: info@sainternans.com
In USA tel: Toll Free 800-323-5463
or E. mail: USA@irelandsbluebook.com

How to find:
One mile south of Donegal town on R267, which is the southern connection from N15 to Donegal town.

DONEGAL, CO. DONEGAL

GLASSDRUMMAN LODGE
COUNTRY HOUSE AND RESTAURANT

Glassdrumman Lodge lies in the heart of the ancient 'Kingdom of Mourne', on the Co. Down coast. This majestic friendly range of mountains, rich in history and legend, is one of the most picturesque districts in the island of Ireland. The magnificent forests of Tollymore and Castlewellan are situated within a short distance.

The Lodge is owned by Graeme and Joan Hall whose philosophy is 'Simple Excellence' and have already gained a widespread reputation and acclaim for its food and elegance. The peaceful atmosphere is enhanced by gastronomic delights, fresh produce from the gardens, and local ports supplying fresh sea and shellfish – oysters a speciality. This family run restaurant is highly recommended by many international good food and hotel guides.

There are ten well appointed bedrooms en suite, 24-hour room service, direct dial telephone, colour tv, overnight laundry and a secretarial service. Ideal facilities for small executive conferences.

In the grounds there is a one acre fly fishing lake, well stocked with rainbow trout, for guests who think walking on the local beaches or hiking in the Mournes is too energetic.

The Hall family would be happy to arrange golf at the famous Royal County Down Golf Course, which is fifteen minutes drive away.

AA Rating: Two Red Star Hotel and Two Red Star Restaurant.

Number of Bedrooms: 8 | Number of Suites: 2 | Guesthouse ★ ★ ★

Glassdrumman Lodge, Mill Road, Annalong, Co. Down, N. Ireland BT34 4RH.
Tel: 028 437 68451.
Fax: 028 437 67041.
From Rep. of Ireland:0044-28-437-68451
E. Mail: info@glassdrummanlodge.com
Proprietors: Graeme & Joan Hall

Map Reference: 20.
Open all year.
Low season (Oct-Apr): Single: £60-£80.
Double: £80-£100. Suite: £100-£130.
High season (Apr-Oct): Single: £90-£110.
Double: £100-£135. Suite: £135-£150.
Dinner from Stg£27.50-Stg£35pp. Dinner available to non-residents by reservation.

Reservations:
US Reps Tel. Toll Free: 800-323-5463, or E mail: usa@irelandsbluebook.com or dial Glassdrumman direct.
How to find:
From Dublin: to Newry, then A2 coast road to Warrenpoint, Kilkeel, Annalong, turn left at Halfway House into Mill Road.
From Belfast: to Newcastle, then A2 coast road towards Kilkeel, turn right at Halfway House into Mill Road, Annalong.
ANNALONG, CO. DOWN.

GLIN CASTLE

HISTORIC HOUSE

Glin Castle, one of Ireland's most historic properties, has been in the FitzGerald family, hereditary Knights of Glin, for over 700 years. The castle with its superb interiors, decorative plasterwork, and collections of Irish furniture and paintings, stands on the bank of the River Shannon surrounded by formal gardens and parkland and in the middle of 500 acres of woodland and dairy farm. One hour's drive from Shannon airport, half an hour from Ballybunion championship golf course and within easy reach of three other such courses, including the new Greg Norman links course, Doonbeg. The Ring of Kerry, Dingle Peninsula and the wonders of Co. Clare including the Cliffs of Moher and the Burren (via the nearby car ferry) make Glin a superb centre for exploring southwest Ireland.

We offer the best in Irish Country House cuisine, using fresh vegetables and fruit from the beautifully kept walled kitchen garden, locally produced meat and poultry and freshly caught fish. Hard tennis court and croquet lawn are in the gardens. Claypigeon shooting and archery can be arranged on site. Glin village, which boasts the most traditional pub in Ireland, is at the front gate.

Number of Bedrooms: 15 | Specialist Accommodation: Historic House

Glin Castle, Glin, Co. Limerick.
Tel: 068-34173.
Fax: 068-34364.
E. Mail: knight@iol.ie
Web site: www.glincastle.com
Proprietors: Desmond & Olda FitzGerald
Manager: Bob Duff

Map Reference: 21.
Open: 29 March – 3 November.
Room & Breakfast – Standard room €280.
Superior room €360. Deluxe room €440.
Dinner: €48 per person from 7.00-9.30pm.
Credit Cards: Amex, Visa, MasterCard, Diners.
Gratuities at guests discretion.

Reservations:
US Reps Tel. Toll Free: 800-323-5463,
or E mail: usa@irelandsbluebook.com
or direct with Castle. GDS Code: LM.
How to find:
On the picturesque N69 between Foynes and Tarbert. From Shannon follow signs for Cork and Tralee and then the N69 for 32 miles along the south bank of the river. Turn left into Glin village off the main road and right at the top of the square.
GLIN, CO. LIMERICK.

GREGANS CASTLE
COUNTRY HOUSE AND RESTAURANT

"Excellence through family ownership for 28 years"

With breathtaking views across the Burren, perhaps Ireland's most surprising limestone landscape, Gregans Castle Hotel, at the foot of the Corkscrew Hill, enjoys a splendid view towards Galway Bay.

This is a special area with treasures for the botanist and explorer of historic ruins. Peter, Moira and Simon Haden own and manage this oasis, where hospitality, good food, comfort, peace and quiet are the themes.

All bedrooms have every comfort and no televisions. The superior rooms and suites are particularly commodious, and are especially recommended. Some of these are at the ground floor level.

A large borrowed landscape garden and rural setting, ensure a peaceful harmony. Non residents are welcome for daytime food, and for dinner in the dining room. Golf at Lahinch and Doonbeg, horse back riding, cycling and walking in the Burren, and close-by short ferry service to the Aran Islands, from Doolin, are just a few of the many things to do. E-mail access for guests.

Classification 2004: AA Red Stars and Rosettes, RAC Blue Ribbon, Karen Brown recommended, Good Hotel Guide, Good Food Guide.

Number of Bedrooms: 15 | Number of Suites: 6 | Hotel ★ ★ ★ ★

Gregans Castle Hotel, Ballyvaughan, Co. Clare.
E. Mail: res@gregans.ie
Web Site: www.gregans.ie
Proprietors: The Haden Family
Map Reference: 22.
Open: late March to end of October.
Bed & Irish breakfast, Low season €80-€160;
Single Supplement €55-€115.
Bed & Irish breakfast, High season €99-€230;
Single Supplement €79-€200.
Dinner €36-€52.
All taxes included in prices.
Credit card for guarantee: Visa, Mastercard, Amex.
Cancellation Policy: Three days.

Reservations:
Instant confirmation available now
on-line at www.gregans.ie
Phone, Fax, E. Mail direct to hotel with guarantee.
Tel. within Ireland: 065 7077 005
Tel. outside Ireland: +353 65 7077 005
Fax: Above prefix codes, then: 7077 111
USA Reservations systems: 1800-323-5463
or E mail: usa@irelandsbluebook.com
**One hour's scenic drive from Shannon
Airport. Early check in possible.**
How to find:
On the inland road N67, just
3.5 miles south of Ballyvaughan:

NR. BALLYVAUGHAN, CO. CLARE

HUNTER'S HOTEL
COUNTRY HOUSE AND RESTAURANT

One of Ireland's oldest coaching inns, now in the 5th generation of the same family with a long standing tradition of friendliness, hospitality and good food. Its picturesque gardens along the banks of the river Vartry provide a haven from the world at large, and a delightful setting for a delicious afternoon tea, or a pre-lunch or dinner drink.

The hotel is an ideal base from which to visit Mount Usher Gardens, Powerscourt Gardens, Russborough House, Glendalough and the other attractions of Co. Wicklow, "The Garden of Ireland", where a Garden Festival is held every year in May/June.

Local amenities include fifteen 18 hole golf courses within a half hour's drive, most notably Druid's Glen and the European. Horse riding and hill walking are other pursuits which can be arranged for guests. Hunter's has 16 charming en suite bedrooms, comfortably furnished with antiques. Conference facilities are available for groups of up to 30 people. Hunter's is within one hour's drive from Dublin, and within two hour's drive from Rosslare.

Number of Bedrooms: 16 | Hotel ★ ★ ★

Hunter's Hotel, Newrath Bridge, Rathnew, Co. Wicklow.
Tel: 0404-40106. Fax: 0404-40338.
E. Mail: reception@hunters.ie
Web site: www.hunters.ie
Proprietors: Gelletlie Family

Map Reference: 23.
Closed 24, 25 and 26 December.
Bed & breakfast from €95-€115.
Dinner from €42 from 7.30-9.00pm.
Luncheon €22 from 1.00-3.00pm.
Afternoon tea from €6.50.
No service charge.
French spoken.

American Express, Visa, MasterCard credit cards accepted.

Reservations:
Tel. +353 404 40106.
US Reps Tel. Toll Free: 800-323-5463
or E mail: usa@irelandsbluebook.com

How to find:
From Dublin: Turn left off N11 at the bridge in Ashford. Then 1.5mls. From Wexford/ Rosslare: Turn right off N11 on leaving Rathnew. Then 0.5 ml.

RATHNEW, CO. WICKLOW.

St. John's
COUNTRY HOUSE AND RESTAURANT

In the remote northwest corner of Ireland, situated by the shores of Lough Swilly on the Inishowen Peninsula, St. John's Country House and Restaurant enjoys spectacular views of Inch Island and the Donegal Highlands.

St. John's was built in 1785 and restored by its present owners, retaining all the elegance and charm of country house living. Opened as a restaurant in 1980, using fresh local produce in season, Donegal mountain lamb, home-made breads and of course fresh fish and local seafood feature highly on the menu. The restaurant now has international acclaim with its many awards.

A cosy bar with turf fire and now with 5 well appointed en suite bedrooms, makes St. John's an ideal base to experience the splendid isolation of mountain and ocean.

Lots to do. Visit Malin Head, Ireland's most northern point, five local golf courses, endless beaches, the historic city of Derry, Giants Causeway. Good salmon and trout fishing from March 1st to 30th September.

Do you know that the spectacular ring fort of Grianan of Aileach dates from around 1700 BC. Up here it's different.

Number of Bedrooms: 5 | Guesthouse ★ ★ ★ ★

St. John's Country House and Restaurant
Fahan, Inishowen, Co. Donegal.
Tel: 00 353 74 9360289.
Fax: 00 353 74 9360612.
Email: stjohnsrestaurant@eircom.net
Web site: http://homepage.eircom.net/
~stjohnscountryhouse/
Proprietors: Reg Ryan and Phil McAfee

Map Reference: 24.
Bed and full Irish breakfast from €60-€100 pps. Single supplement €20.
Dinner €40 – 7.30pm to 9.00pm.
All major Credit cards accepted.
Open mid-March – end October 2004

Reservations:
Direct from USA 011 353 77 60289
or Toll Free: 800-323-5463
or E mail: usa@irelandsbluebook.com
From UK 00 353 74 9360289.
By Fax: 00 353 74 9360612.

How to find:
Situated in the village of Fahan on the main Derry to Buncrana Road R238.

FAHAN, CO. DONEGAL

KING SITRIC

FISH RESTAURANT AND ACCOMMODATION

Established in 1971, Aidan and Joan MacManus have earned an international reputation for fresh seafood in their harbour-side restaurant in the picturesque fishing village of Howth. In 1999, they extensively rebuilt their old Harbour Master's house, relocating the restaurant to the first floor with panoramic sea-views, and adding eight guest bedrooms. All the bedrooms are named after Lighthouses and have sea-views.

Fresh fish landed daily on Howth Pier, oysters and mussels from the west, lobster caught by our own fishermen in Balscadden Bay are among our specialities. Enjoy a pre-dinner drink in our Wine Cellar while choosing your wine from our extensive Wine List. Good Food Guide 2003 "Outstanding Wine Cellar".

We are situated in the golfing heartland of North County Dublin and for sailors, Howth Marina is three minutes walk. Enjoy a gentle stroll on the Pier before breakfast or a more energetic hike on the unspoiled Cliff Path and the trails of Howth Head, which has recently been the subject of a Special Area Amenity Order. For business, shopping or sightseeing, Dublin City is only 25 minutes by Dart. Dublin Airport 20 minutes.

Number of Bedrooms: 8 | Guesthouse ★ ★ ★ ★

King Sitric, Fish Restaurant & Accommodation, East Pier, Howth, Co. Dublin.
Tel: 01-832 5235, 01-832 6729.
Fax: 01-839 2442.
E. Mail: info@kingsitric.ie
Web site: www.kingsitric.ie
Proprietors: Aidan & Joan MacManus

Map Reference: 25.
Closed last two weeks January, few days at Christmas. Restaurant closed Sundays and Bank Holidays.
Bed & Breakfast from €66-€100 per person sharing all year.
Single supplement €30

Dinner 2004 €52
Lunch from €22
Private dining.
Credit cards: Visa/Amex/Access.
Children welcome.
Reservations: Direct with house.
In USA Tel. Toll Free: 800-323-5463,
or E mail: usa@irelandsbluebook.com
How to find:
All the way across the
Harbour-front,
end of the road.

HOWTH, CO. DUBLIN.

L'ECRIVAIN
RESTAURANT

L'Ecrivain Restaurant, 109a Lower Baggot Street, Dublin 2, in the heart of Georgian Dublin. This modern, contemporary restaurant is run by Chef, Derry Clarke and his wife, Sallyanne, has been established since July 1989.

This award-winning restaurant, Evian/Food & Wine Magazine Best Restaurant Award 2003 & 2002; Best Dublin Restaurant Award 2003; Best Chef 2003.

The restaurant has built itself a reputation for innovative cooking Irish/French style using the very best of Irish produce from small indigenous producers all in season. It is also well known for its fish, which is caught all over Ireland on the same day as used. Derry Clarke is renowned for his culinary expertise, and together with his team of chefs and front of house team, l'Ecrivain is an experience not to be missed.

l'Ecrivain Restaurant, 109a Lower Baggot Street, Dublin 2.

Tel: 00 353 1 6611919.
Fax: 00 353 1 6610617.
E. Mail: enquiries@lecrivain.com
Web site: www.lecrivain.com
Proprietors: Derry and Sally Anne Clarke.

Map Reference: 26.
Extensive Wine List and Cocktail List available.
Table d'Hote and A la Carte Menus available.
Set Lunch Menus. Gift Vouchers available.
Main Restaurant seats 100.
The Malt Room – Private Dining Room seats

18 comfortably, 20 people max.
Lunch: Monday to Friday 12.30 to 2.00pm.
Dinner: Monday to Thursday 7.00 to 10.30pm
Friday and Saturday 7.00 to 11.00pm.
Reservations recommended.
In USA tel: Toll Free 800-323-5463
or E. mail: USA@irelandsbluebook.com

DUBLIN, CO. DUBLIN.

LISDONAGH HOUSE

COUNTRY HOUSE

Lisdonagh House is located 20 minutes from Galway City in a glorious tranquil setting. The house is early Georgian with commanding views over Lough Hackett. There are over 100 acres of woodland on the estate where guests can meander on country walks. Coarse fishing and horse riding can be arranged. It is possible to hunt with the North Galway Blazers in season. Historic and scenic tours may be organised by request.

Your hosts, John and Finola Cooke, have restored the house to a supremely comfortable standard whilst retaining all the period features. The oval entrance hall has murals depicting the four virtues dating from 1790. The bedrooms are named after prominent Irish artists and writers.

Each evening at dinner a menu "surprise" is served to guests. The cooking is superb, innovatively using the best of local produce. Fresh seafood is a speciality. A kitchen garden supplies the house with vegetables and herbs. We cater for vegetarian and special food requirements.

A warm welcome is extended to guests at Lisdonagh. It is a terrific vantage point from which to explore Connemara, Cong, Yeats Country and the Aran Islands. It is situated close to some of the finest golf courses in the West of Ireland. Equally it is an ideal choice for a quiet relaxing time in a beautiful setting.

Number of Bedrooms: 10 | Guesthouse/Historic House ★ ★ ★ ★

**Lisdonagh House, Caherlistrane,
Near Headford, Co. Galway.**
Tel: +353 93-31163. Fax: +353 93-31528
E. Mail: cooke@lisdonagh.com
Web site: www.lisdonagh.com
Proprietor: John and Finola Cooke
Map Reference: 27.
Bed & Breakfast: from €70-€120pps.
Single supplement €30.
Dinner: Set Menu €40 at 8.00 pm.
Open May 1 - October 31
Credit Cards: Mastercard, Visa.
Reservations: Direct with the house.
In USA Tel. Toll Free: 800-323-5463,
or E mail: usa@irelandsbluebook.com

How to find: From South/Dublin: Take N17
towards Sligo. Approx. 11 miles from
Claregalway turn left at R333 through Belclare
to Caherlistrane. In Caherlistrane, turn right at
Queally's pub, approx. 1.5 miles turn left down
signed road. From Galway: Take N84 to
Headford. In Headford turn right at
"Anglers Rest", continue on N84
for approx 3 miles, turn right
for Lisdonagh House.
Additional Information:
Exclusive parties catered
for by arrangement.

CAHERLISTRANE, CO. GALWAY

27

LONGUEVILLE HOUSE

AND PRESIDENTS' RESTAURANT

Set in 500 acres of wooded estate in the heart of the Blackwater Valley, Longueville House is a 1720 Georgian Heritage Mansion owned and run by the O'Callaghan family.

Longueville is an ideal base for touring or golfing in the scenic southwest, and provides a peaceful and tranquil setting for those who wish to relax or laze by the fire. The Longueville estate offers a variety of activities to guests, including salmon and brown trout fishing on the River Blackwater, walk up shoots between the months of November and January and scenic walks throughout the estate.

The Presidents Restaurant, presents a menu offering fresh produce from the garden, farm and river, and the kitchen is supervised by William O'Callaghan, a combination that is widely commended in various international food guides and magazines. Guests may enjoy dining in the recently restored Victorian Turner Conservatory (1862) which has been beautifully and aesthetically restored to its former glory.

Longueville provides an atmosphere and setting ideal as a venue for residential wedding parties, business meetings and prestigious events.

Number of Bedrooms: 13 | Number of Junior Suites: 7 | Listed Heritage Hotel Property ★ ★ ★ ★

Longueville House and Presidents' Restaurant, Mallow, Co. Cork.
Tel: 022-47156. Fax: 022-47459.
E. Mail: info@longuevillehouse.ie
Web site: www.longuevillehouse.ie
Proprietors: The O'Callaghan Family

Map Reference: 28.
Open: 28 December 2003 – 20 December 2004.
Closed 15 February 2004 – 4 March 2004.
Bed & Breakfast €90-€147.50 pps low season;
€100-€180 pps high season. Single Supplement
€55 in standard room. Dinner from €50-€65 from
6.30-9.00pm Table d'Hôte Menu. Vegetarians and
Vegans welcome. All major Credit Cards accepted.
• Non-smoking rooms and restaurants
• Private dining room takes 18

• Conference centre takes 45
• Syndicate room for business/board meetings
• Exclusive residential wedding parties 110 max.
• Out of season house parties /shooting parties
• Special shoulder season breaks
• Gift vouchers for overnight stays/short breaks
Reservations: E. Mail: info@longuevillehouse.ie
In USA Tel. Toll Free: 800-323-5463,
or E mail: usa@irelandsbluebook.com
GDS Code: Apollo/Galileo/Sabre/
Amadeus/Worldspan.
How to find:
3 miles west of Mallow on the
N72 to Killarney. Take Ballyclough
junction to the right and hotel
entrance is 100 yards on left side.

MALLOW, CO. CORK.

MARLFIELD HOUSE
COUNTRY HOUSE AND RESTAURANT

Marlfield House is a fine Regency period house set amidst 36 acres of grounds and gardens and just a few minutes from miles of sandy beaches. Formerly the residence of the Earls of Courtown, it was built in the 1830's and opened to guests by the Bowe family in 1978. The 20 bedrooms are filled with flowers and fine antiques, paintings and works of art. All have marble bathrooms, many overlook the gardens and there are six sumptuous state rooms overlooking the lake. Enjoy tennis, croquet or a wander through the grounds which include woodlands, extensive kitchen and rose gardens and a lake and wildfowl reserve. The kitchen garden provides much of the produce for our highly acclaimed Conservatory diningroom which has gained many accolades over the years.

Situated just outside Gorey on the Courtown road, Marlfield is 65 miles south of Dublin and 28 miles north of Wexford. It is located within 20 minutes of 6 different golf clubs including, the European, Woodenbridge, Seafield and Coolattin and 45 minutes from Druids Glen Golf Club. Marlfield provides the ideal location for discovering Wicklow, "The Garden of Ireland", the medieval city of Kilkenny and Waterford Crystal.

Marlfield has gained many awards over the years including The Good Hotel Guide Caesar Award, Relais et Chateaux Best Breakfast Award, it was listed in Andrew Harper's Hideaway Report "Best 25 Hotels in the World", AA Three Red Stars and Three Red Rosettes, RAC Gold Ribbon and Johansen's Country Hotel of the Year.

Number of Bedrooms: 14 | Number of State Rooms 6

Marlfield House, Gorey, Co. Wexford.
Tel: 353 (0)55-21124. Fax: 353 (0)55-21572.
E. Mail: info@marlfieldhouse.ie
Web site: www.marlfieldhouse.com

Proprietors: The Bowe Family
Map Reference: 29.
Open: 1 February to mid-December.
Bed & Breakfast from €118 pps low season; from €128 pps high season.
State rooms from €213 pps-€365 pps
Single rooms from €130 and single supplement available on request.
Dinner is available for non-residents also and is from €56. Library snacks Monday to Saturday and Sunday lunch in the diningroom.
All major credit cards accepted.
Wheelchair accessible. Dog friendly.

Reservations:
Direct with the house.
In USA Tel. Toll Free: 800-323-5463,
or E mail: usa@irelandsbluebook.com

How to find:
2km from Gorey on Courtown Road R742.

Extra information:
• Excellent venue for small conferences.
• Special low season rates available on request.
• Exclusive take over weddings of up to 80 catered for.
• Gift vouchers available.
• Perfect for take over parties.

GOREY, CO. WEXFORD.

MOY HOUSE
COUNTRY HOUSE

The sensitive restoration of this early 19th century estate recreates a contemporary and eclectic ambience for today's traveller in search of a tranquil respite with natural and warm Irish hospitality. Comprising of 15 acres and with commanding hilltop views over Lahinch Bay, the Estate is enhanced by mature woodland and the meandering River Moy.

Each of the nine oversized, comfortable bedrooms are individually crafted with a mixture of classic and contemporary functionalism and aesthetics. The signature statement for the House are the guest bedrooms, a number of which have free-standing original cast iron baths.

The residential ambience is complemented by a number of private spaces dispersed throughout the House; from the traditional Drawing Room to the Zen-feel of the lower Library area. The warm and snug-like Dining Room offers the best of contemporary Irish fayre for both breakfast and dinner.

Overlooking some of the best surfing beaches in Ireland, and within close proximity to both Lahinch and Doonbeg links courses, Moy House is the ideal centre for exploring the Cliffs of Moher and nature's glorious Burren area, renowned for its wild and abundant flora and fauna.

Winner of the "Country House of the Year Award 2003" – Georgina Campbell/Jameson Guide.

Number of Bedrooms: 9 | Guesthouse ★ ★ ★ ★

Moy House, Lahinch, Co. Clare.
Tel: 00353 (0)65-708 2800.
Fax: 00353 (0)65-708 2500.
E. Mail: moyhouse@eircom.net
Web site: www.moyhouse.com
Proprietor: Antoin O'Looney
Manager: Bernie Merry.

Map Reference: 30.
1st January to 1st March – open weekends only. From 1st March – open full time.
Bed & Breakfast €97.50 pps low season to €114.50 pps high season. Single and group rates available on request. Special offers available from Nov to May.
All rates include taxes.

There is no service charge.
Dinner €45.

Reservations:
In USA Tel. Toll Free: 800-323-5463, or E mail: usa@irelandsbluebook.com through the Moy House web site at www.moyhouse.com or direct with the house.

How to find: Moy House is located about one mile out of Lahinch town, on the Milltown Malbay road. Shannon Airport – 1 hr drive.

LAHINCH, CO. CLARE.

Moyglare Manor

COUNTRY HOUSE AND RESTAURANT

Ireland's nearest Country House Hotel to the Airport. Eighteen miles from Dublin and half a mile of a tree-lined avenue lead to this unique Georgian House with its majestic exterior holding court over beautiful parklands.

Enjoy the relaxed homely atmosphere of this opulent family-run Grade A Hotel, which is renowned worldwide for its magnificent decor and antique furnishings.

The luxurious en suite bedrooms, each with their own particular views of the surrounding countryside, are individually styled with elegant period furniture including romantic four posters. Modern amenities available here have detracted nothing from the ambience of a past era.

Experience the excellent cuisine in candlelit, intimate dining rooms. An exhaustive wine list, cosy old world charm, together with a very warm and friendly welcome will ensure your visit is momentous. Recommended by all leading Hotel and Good Food Guides. Blue Ribbon award 2000, 2001, 2002 and 2003, AA Rosette Awards for 1997, '98, '99, 2000, '01, '02 and '03. Winner of Wine List of the Year 1999.

Four golf courses within 10 miles; tennis court; horse riding and fox hunting available nearby.

Small conferences catered for 2-30 delegates. Confidentiality, unhurried appointments, we strive to meet all company requisitions.

Number of Bedrooms: 16 | Number of Suites: 1

Moyglare Manor, Maynooth, Co. Kildare.
Tel: 01-628 6351. Fax: 01-628 5405.
E. Mail: info@moyglaremanor.ie
or reservations@moyglaremanor.ie
Web site: www.moyglaremanor.ie
Proprietor: Norah Devlin.
Manager: Shay Curran and Anna Lisa Curran.

Map Reference: 31.
Open: All year except 3 days at Christmas.
Bed & Breakfast from €125 pps all year round. Single Supplement €25.
12.5% service charge.
Dinner €55.
All major credit cards accepted.

Wheelchair facilities.
Children under 12 not catered for.

Reservations:
In USA Tel. Toll Free: 800-323-5463,
or E mail: usa@irelandsbluebook.com
or direct with House. GDS Code: LM.

How to find: Travelling west on N4/M4 through Maynooth, keep right at Church – 2km.
Coordinates of Helicopter
Landing Area:
N53° 24'.4   W006° 36'.4

MAYNOOTH, CO. KILDARE.

THE MUSTARD SEED AT ECHO LODGE
COUNTRY HOUSE AND RESTAURANT

Nestled in the heart of the County Limerick countryside is The Mustard Seed at Echo Lodge, a converted 19th century convent. Set on ten acres, the celebrated country house is surrounded by mature trees, orchard and kitchen garden where fresh herbs and vegetables are gathered daily for the preparation of dinner.

The talented kitchen brigade create exquisite culinary delights for the discerning diners. An extensive wine list compliments the enticing menu. The Mustard Seed also welcomes non-residents for dinner and has long been highly acclaimed for attracting lovers of good food and wine from around the globe.

Each of the seventeen bedrooms are individually decorated combining traditional antique furnishings and modern facilities. Good taste prevails and an interesting collection of books fills the library downstairs for a rainy day by the fire. A small sauna and massage room are available for guests in the house.

The Mustard Seed at Echo Lodge is an ideal base for touring the south west region. The Dingle Peninsula, Killarney and the Ring of Kerry, the Cliffs of Moher and the Burren are all within driving distance. For the golf enthusiast, a choice of four courses are within thirty minutes drive of the house. Horse riding, fishing and garden visits can all be arranged nearby.

Number of Bedrooms: 14 | Number of Suites: 3 | Hotel ★ ★ ★ ★

The Mustard Seed at Echo Lodge,
Ballingarry, Co. Limerick.
Tel: 069-68508. Fax: 069-68511
E. Mail: mustard@indigo.ie
Web Site: www.mustardseed.ie
Proprietor: Daniel Mullane.

Map Reference: 32.
Open: All year round.
Closed 24-26 December.
B&B from €86-€140. Rates apply all year round. Single Supplement €20-€40.
Dinner €50 per person. Special spring and winter break rates on request.

Reservations: Direct with the House.
In USA Tel. Toll Free: 800-323-5463,
or E mail: usa@irelandsbluebook.com

How to find: From Limerick: From the top of Adare village, take the N21 Killarney Road for half a mile. Turn left at the first road junction to the left and follow the signposts to Ballingarry. From Kerry: Travel along the N21. Look for signs for Rathkeale. In Rathkeale town, follow the R518 for four miles to Ballingarry village

BALLINGARRY CO. LIMERICK

NEWPORT HOUSE
COUNTRY HOUSE AND RESTAURANT

Historic Georgian House in gardens and park adjoining the town and overlooking the Newport river and quay. For two hundred years it was the home of the O'Donnells, once the Earls of Tir Connell.

Famous as an angling centre Newport House offers preserved salmon and sea trout fishing on the Newport river (8 miles) and Lough Beltra. Salmon fishing is available on nearby Loughs Feeagh, Furnace, Conn and Mask. Golf is available at Westport championship course and at Mulrany; also horse riding and pony trekking with supervised instruction.

The cuisine is based on fresh local produce. Our home smoked wild salmon and fresh seafood are specialities of the house. The food is complemented by an extensive cellar which includes many of the classical vintages.

The house is furnished with many fine antiques and paintings which provide an elegant setting for a quiet and relaxing holiday.

Number of Bedrooms: 18

Newport House, Newport, Co. Mayo.
Tel: 098-41222. Fax: 098-41613.
E. Mail: info@newporthouse.ie
Web site: www.newporthouse.ie
Proprietors: Kieran & Thelma Thompson.
Map Reference: 33.
Open: 19 March – 5 October.
Bed & Breakfast from €104-€140 low season; from €115-€151 high season. Single Supplement €24 Superior Room Supplement €22. Dinner €55 from 7.00pm to last orders 9.30pm.
Prices inclusive of VAT.

Credit Cards: Visa/MasterCard/ American Express and Diners.
French spoken.

Reservations:
By post, Telephone, Fax and E. Mail.
In USA Tel. Toll Free: 800-323-5463, or E mail: usa@irelandsbluebook.com or direct with House.

How to find:
In the village of Newport.

NEWPORT, CO. MAYO

33

PARK HOTEL KENMARE
COUNTRY HOUSE AND RESTAURANT

Since 1897 many world travellers have enjoyed the pleasure of the Park Hotel Kenmare and its renowned restaurant. Set in a heavenly location overlooking Kenmare Bay the hotel is in the heart of Ireland's most scenic countryside. All accommodations are spacious with sitting area, antique furnishings and original art while Deluxe and Suites enjoy a full sea view or private veranda.

Home to the Deluxe Destination Spa SÁMAS; guests can experience the virtues of a true spa. This special and quite unique place blends healing and therapeutic traditions from the East and West with the life inspiring scenery of Kerry to revive the body, mind and soul.

The Hotel's lifeStyle ProgrAmmes combine traditional Country House elegance with mental and physical relaxation to provide a true indulgence of the senses. Daily activities include golf, fishing, jogging, flora/fauna and heritage walks, hiking, Tai-Chi, Yoga, meditation, golf and fishing.

Come to this special corner of Ireland and be reborn.

Number of Bedrooms: 40 | Number of Suites: 9 | Hotel ★ ★ ★ ★

Park Hotel Kenmare, Kenmare, Co. Kerry.
Tel: +353-64-41200.
Fax: +353-64-41402.
E. Mail: info@parkkenmare.com
Web site: www.parkkenmare.com
Proprietor: Mr. Francis Brennan
General Manager: Mr. John Brennan
Map Reference: 34.
Open: 6 February – 28 November;
Christmas and New Year.
Double/Twin €149-€348 pps B&B incl. of tax.
Dinner €64.
Credit Cards: All major credit cards accepted.
Wheelchair facilities.

Children welcome.
French/German spoken.
Reservations:
In USA Tel. Toll Free: 800-323-5463,
or E mail: usa@irelandsbluebook.com
Tel: +353 64 41200
Fax: +353 64 41402
E. Mail: info@parkkenmare.com
How to find:
"Top of Town".

KENMARE, CO. KERRY

34

RATHMULLAN HOUSE
COUNTRY HOUSE AND RESTAURANT

Rathmullan House, a gracious Georgian house built in the 1780s, enjoys an unrivalled location overlooking the shores of Lough Swilly. Set in ten acres, its beautifully landscaped gardens stretch down to a two mile sandy beach.

Elegant spacious lounges furnished with antiques, paintings and open fires, provide slumbering comfort.

Each of the tastefully decorated bedrooms have their own distinctive style and character, many of which provide delightful views over the garden and several with balconies. The restaurant, which has won critical acclaim from numerous guides, serves award-winning food from a daily changing menu and is inspired by the use of the finest local produce.

Amenities: indoor heated swimming pool, steam room, masseuse, tennis and croquet. Boat available to explore Lough Swilly. Horse-riding and golfing locally. Discover national heritage, scenic drives, hill walking and within reach of Giants Causeway.

Number of Bedrooms: 24 | Hotel ★ ★ ★ ★

Rathmullan House, Rathmullan, Co. Donegal.
Tel: 074-9158188. Fax: 074-9158200.
E. Mail: info@rathmullanhouse.com
Web site: www.rathmullanhouse.com
Proprietors: The Wheeler Family

Map Reference: 35.
Open from 1st April.
Bed & Breakfast from €80-€125 pp low season;
€105-€125 pp high season. Single rooms from €80.
Dinner €45.
10% Service charge.
Reservations advisable for non-residents.
All major cards accepted.
Dogs welcome with prior arrangement.
• Special rates available for longer stays.
• Ground floor bedrooms.
• Children welcome.

• House parties and corporate events catered for low season.

Reservations: Direct with the house by phone, fax and E. Mail. From UK Tel: 00-353-74-9158188
From UK Fax: 00-353-74-9158200
From USA Tel: 011-353-74-9158188
US Reps Tel. Toll Free: 800-323-5463. GDS: LM
or E mail: usa@irelandsbluebook.com

How to find: From Letterkenny go to Ramelton. Turn right at bridge to Rathmullan. Through village gates on the right.
Dublin 3.5-4 hours via N2 and A5.
Belfast 2 hours via A6.
City of Derry Airport 1 hour.
RATHMULLAN, CO. DONEGAL.

RATHSALLAGH HOUSE

COUNTRY HOUSE AND RESTAURANT

Converted from Queen Anne stables in 1798, Rathsallagh is a large comfortable house situated in 530 acres of peaceful parkland with a walled garden and its own 18-hole Championship Golf Course. It is central to some of the most beautiful countryside in eastern Ireland. Glendalough, the Wicklow mountains, the Japanese Gardens & National Stud and the Curragh, and Punchestown racecourse are all close by, yet Dublin is less than one hour's drive.

The O'Flynn family and their staff look forward to welcoming you to Rathsallagh. The atmosphere is happy and relaxed with log and turf fires, central heating throughout and luxurious bedrooms all with en suite bathrooms.

The food is Country House cooking at its best and is organically produced by local growers and in Rathsallagh's gardens. Game in season and fresh fish from the Wexford coast are specialities. In addition to winning the National breakfast awards four times, Rathsallagh was also voted Country House of the Year 2000 and Country House Restaurant of the Year 2002.

Amenities: 4 Star Grade A Country House, 18-hole Championship Golf Course, Heated Indoor Swimming Pool, Sauna & Spa Room, Billiard table, Tennis and Croquet. Clay Pigeon Shooting with C.P.S.A. Club Coach, Archery by prior arrangement. Fully equipped Conference Rooms. Helipad.

Number of Bedrooms: 29

Rathsallagh House, Dunlavin, Co. Wicklow.
Tel: 045-403112.
Fax: 045-403343.
E. Mail: info@rathsallagh.com
Web site: www.rathsallagh.com
Proprietor: The O'Flynn Family
Map Reference: 36.
Open: All year except Christmas.
Bed & Breakfast from €125-€145 pps. No service charge.
Single Supplement €40-€65.
Dinner from €50-€65.
Golf for residents from €45-€65.
All major credit cards accepted.
Dogs welcome strictly by prior reservation.

Children under 12 not catered for.
German and French spoken.
Wheelchair facilities.

Reservations:
In USA Tel. Toll Free: 800-323-5463,
or E mail: usa@irelandsbluebook.com
GDS Code: LM.
Direct with Rathsallagh House.

How to find:
Signposted in Dunlavin village. 1 hour from Dublin. 15 miles Naas or Curragh.

DUNLAVIN, CO. WICKLOW (WEST).

Restaurant Patrick Guilbaud

Patrick Guilbaud created his restaurant in 1981 – 22 years ago – Restaurant Patrick Guilbaud is Ireland's top restaurant, holder of two Michelin stars as well as virtually all the top national and international awards. It is situated in an 18th century Georgian Townhouse adjoining the Merrion Hotel. It houses an impressive collection of Irish Art.

This bright, elegant restaurant, run by Stephane Robin, serves modern classic cuisine using the best Irish produce in season. The restaurant has played host to many famous guests over the past 22 years. Chef Guillaume Lebrun's signature dishes include the Lobster Ravioli, Roast Challans Duck for two, Assiette Gourmande au Chocolat. Everything is made on the premises from the wonderful selection of breads to the petit fours. The wine list, created by Charles Derain, is very impressive in both its depth and its range – do take time to peruse it.

The table d'hote lunch menu at €30 is very popular with both the business community and tourists alike and is described as one of Dublin's best kept secrets! Of course our dinner menu at €79 is hugely desirable and booking is essential! As well as the A la Carte, you might also like to sample our Tasting Menu which allows you to try our version of typical Irish dishes.

Number of Covers: 85

Restaurant Patrick Guilbaud,
21 Upper Merrion Street, Dublin 2.
Tel: 01-6764 192.
Fax: 01-6610 052.
E. Mail: restaurantpatrickguilbaud@eircom.net
Website: www.restaurantpatrickguilbaud.ie
Proprietor: Patrick Guilbaud
Chef: Guillaume Leburn
Manager: Stephane Robin

Map Reference: 37.
Open: Tuesday to Saturday.
Closed: 25 December – 6 January.
Lunch: 12.30-2.15pm. Dinner: 7.30pm-10.15pm.
Lunch Menu: €30 (2 courses); €45 (3 courses).

Table d'Hote: €79. Tasting Menu: €130.
A la carte available for lunch and dinner.
Reservations:
Direct with the Restaurant.
U.S. Reps: 800-323-5463
or usa@irelandsbluebook.com
How to find:
Opposite Government buildings.
Merrion Street.

DUBLIN, CO. DUBLIN

ROSLEAGUE MANOR
COUNTRY HOUSE AND RESTAURANT

A delightfully situated Georgian house overlooking Ballinakill Bay, which has been discreetly converted into a first-class hotel with a Victorian style conservatory and delightful drawing rooms with open log fires. All of the bedrooms are individually decorated and feature fine antiques and paintings.

Set in 30 acres of secluded woodland to the ocean's edge, Rosleague is a beautifully wooded area on the coast, in the centre of the fabled Connemara and beside Connemara's National Park, an area of some 5,000 acres. Salmon, trout and sea fishing; golf and horseriding all available in the area. Tennis court and billiard table available for guests use.

Winner of the Irish Tourist Board's Award of Excellence and recommended by all the better known Good Food and Hotel Guides, Rosleague is personally supervised by the owners, and all the food is produced locally and prepared by them, with the help of a skilled and experienced staff. The cuisine is based on the freshest and finest of ingredients, with fresh seafood and Connemara lamb a speciality.

Number of Bedrooms: 16 | Number of Suites: 4 | Hotel ★ ★ ★ ★

Rosleague Manor, Letterfrack, Connemara, Co. Galway.
Tel: 095-41101.
Fax: 095-41168.
E. Mail: rosleaguemanor@eircom.net
Web site: www.rosleague.com
Proprietors: Edmund & Mark Foyle

Map Reference: 38.
Open: Open: 15 March – 1 November.
Bed & Breakfast from €75-€100 low season; from €90-€120 high season.
Single supplement €30.
Dinner €45. No service charge.
Exclusive residential wedding parties; 80 max.

Special short break rates on request.
Credit Cards: All major cards accepted.
Children welcome.
French spoken.
Reservations:
Direct to Hotel by tel, fax, post or E. Mail.
In USA Tel. Toll Free: 800-323-5463,
or E mail: usa@irelandsbluebook.com
GDS Code: LM.
How to find:
N59, seven miles north west from Clifden.

LETTERFRACK, CO. GALWAY.

STELLA MARIS HOTEL

COUNTRY HOUSE HOTEL AND RESTAURANT

Experience the Beauty and Tranquility of the Mayo Coastline

Stella Maris was built in 1853 as a Coastguard fortress and subsequently became a convent in 1914. The detailed restoration of this imposing 19th century structure took two years to complete. Antiques are interspersed with comfortable leather furniture to create a 'homely' sense for guests. Visitors enjoy the tranquil setting from the 100-foot conservatory fronting Bunatrahir Bay and picturesque Downpatrick Head, one of the most photogenic sea stacks in Europe.

Proprietor and Executive Chef Frances Kelly oversees the kitchen to ensure a fine dining experience. Stella Maris features its own garden for herbs and vegetables and has been cited for its culinary excellence in several noted publications and guides. Open fires warm the inviting bar and lounge, where guests relax before and after dinner.

Stella Maris is strategically located between the world-renown golf links of Enniscrone and Carne/Belmullet, and is easily accessible to Rosses Point and Westport Golf Clubs. Sea and freshwater fishing are outside the front door. High-quality linens complement tasteful antiques in the individually furnished ocean-front rooms and three-storey suite. Recommended by the Ireland's *Food & Wine Magazine, Georgina Campbell's Guide to the Best Places to Eat, Drink and Stay in Ireland* and most major tour guides.

Number of Bedrooms: 11 | **Number of Suites: 1** | **Handicap Bedrooms: 1** | **Hotel: Newly Registered**

Stella Maris Hotel
Ballycastle, Co. Mayo.
Tel: (Int'l) +353-96-43322.
Fax: (Int'l) +353-96-43965.
E. Mail: Info@StellaMarisIreland.com
Website: www.StellaMarisIreland.com

Proprietor: Frances Kelly & Terence McSweeney

Map Reference: 39.
Open: 8 April – 9 October.
Bed & Breakfast: €90-€115 per person sharing. Single Supplement: €50.
Dinner: a la carte menu, 7.00pm-9.00pm.
Credit Cards: MasterCard / Visa / Laser.
No Service Charge.
Gratuities at discretion of guests.

Reservations:
U.S. Representative: 1-800-323-5463 or
E. mail: usa@irelandsbluebook.com or
Direct with Stella Maris Hotel

How to find:
Stella Maris is located on the ocean, 17 miles west of Ballina and 1.5 miles west of Ballycastle in Co. Mayo.

BALLYCASTLE, CO. MAYO

TINAKILLY HOUSE
COUNTRY HOUSE AND RESTAURANT

"Tinakilly is a beacon to restore hope to the traveler's heart"
   – Bon Appetit Special Collectors Edition.

A romantic secret hideaway, 29 miles south of Dublin, Tinakilly is internationally renowned for splendid fresh food in elegant Victorian surroundings.

Built for Captain Halpin, Commander of the Great Eastern which laid the transatlantic telegraphic cables, Tinakilly is now a luxury hotel and restaurant. The classical Victorian-Italianate architecture is augmented by elegant antique furnishings. Period bedrooms, some with four poster beds, also feature all modern comforts. Junior suites and suites offer breath-taking sea views. The seven acres of Victorian gardens provide perfectly peaceful surroundings.

The award-winning kitchen prepares splendid cuisine from fresh local produce and Tinakilly's own herb garden. Delicious brown and fruit breads are baked daily.

Wicklow boasts stunning mountain drives, Powerscourt and Mount Usher Gardens, Glendalough, excellent golf at nearby Druid's Glen and European Club, horse-riding, mountain hiking and cycling. Splendid weddings and meetings venue.

RAC Blue Ribbon, Hotel Wine List of the Year and Egon Ronay Award winner.

Number of Bedrooms: 51 Including Junior Suites | **Number of Suites: 5** | **Hotel ★ ★ ★ ★**

Tinakilly Country House Hotel & Restaurant,
Wicklow (Rathnew), Co. Wicklow.
Tel: 0404-69274. Fax: 0404-67806.
E. Mail: reservations@tinakilly.ie
Internet: www.tinakilly.ie
Proprietors: Raymond & Josephine Power

Map Reference: 40.
Open: All year except 24-26 December.
Bed & Breakfast from €104-€129 low
season; from €128-€163 high season.
Dinner from €46.
Special Short Break rates on request
Tax and service included.
Credit cards accepted.

Reservations:
Direct to Tinakilly by telephone or fax. Intl.
dialling code: 00-353.
In USA Tel. Toll Free: 800-323-5463 or
800-525-4800,
or E mail: usa@irelandsbluebook.com

How to find: N11/M11 to Rathnew village.
R750 towards Wicklow Town.
29 miles from Dublin city.
35 miles from Dublin Airport.
60 miles from Rosslare ferry
and 20 miles from
Dun Laoghaire ferry.
WICKLOW, (RATHNEW) CO. WICKLOW.

WINEPORT LODGE

LAKESHORE RESTAURANT WITH ROOMS

Wineport Lodge is blissfully located on the edge of Ireland's peaceful Inland Waterways. Housed in an impressive modern cedar-clad structure, it is the perfect place to dine and stay, either for business or pleasure, in an easily accessible destination.

Stunning lake views are afforded from every room and the west-facing balconies ensure sunset is something really special to be savoured. Extra large bathrooms with under-floor heating are a sensual addition and all rooms feature commissioned walnut furniture by leading designer Robert English.

Each guest bedroom is linked exclusively with a wine theme, making Wineport Lodge a must see for the wine lover. The centrepiece of the Lodge is the light-filled double-height Taittinger Champagne Lounge, perfect for relaxing in any time of day.

Business meetings are meticulously attended to in the Tipperary Water Board Room. Glasson Golf Club is just a short boat trip away from our Jetty, and a stroll around the lake begins outside our door. After all that, our resident masseuse is available to soothe your stresses away with a bliss massage.

In the restaurant, Eurotoques Chef Feargal O'Donnell's delicious food is matched by genuine friendly and expert service. An always interesting Menu changes seasonally, and the freshest local produce regularly appears as a daily special.

If you're looking for the ideal hideaway to escape to, then Wineport Lodge is the right place to drop in and revive your jaded soul.

Jameson Guide – Hideaway of the Year Award 2003

Number of Bedrooms: 10

Wineport Lodge, Glasson, Athlone, Co. Westmeath.
Tel: 090 643 9010.
Fax: 090 648 5471.
E. Mail: lodge@wineport.ie
Web site: www.wineport.ie
Proprietors: Ray Byrne & Jane English

Map Reference: 41.
Open: All year round.
Closed: 24-26 December.
Room Rates: €220-€275.
Corporate Rate – Single Occupancy
    (Sunday – Thursday) €175.
Dinner €55.

Special midweek and weekend breaks available
Reservations:
Please call us directly.
In USA tel: Toll Free 800-323-5463
or E. mail: usa@irelandsbluebook.com
How to find:
Take Longford/Cavan exit off the
Dublin/Galway road – fork left
at Dog & Duck pub. Then
1 mile on left hand side.

GLASSON, CO. WESTMEATH

SÁMAS

In a world of its own, overlooking Kenmare Bay and the rugged beauty of the Beara Peninsula.

SÁMAS
awaken the senses

Experience treatments designed for your wellbeing... treatments that encompass philosophies from around the world.

...a deluxe destination spa

Park Hotel Kenmare

Kenmare, Co. Kerry, Ireland
Telephone: +353 64 41200   Facsimile: +353 64 41402
Email: info@parkkenmare.com

See www.samaskenmare.com or www.parkkenmare.com for details

IRELAND
AND IT'S ENVIRONMENT

Ireland is a beautiful country. Research has shown that people come to Ireland to meet the friendly people and enjoy our unspoiled natural landscape. We try as much as we can to keep our country 'clean and green', and we appreciate your co-operation in this matter.

We love to share this beauty with as many people as we can. Therefore, it is in all our interests to maintain and enhance the natural splendour that Ireland is lucky enough to enjoy. Respect for natural amenities is essential in order to sustain this beautiful, unspoiled environment. By leaving the places we visit tidy we can all do our bit to help, thus ensuring that future generations will come to visit a naturally green Ireland too.

- Keep natural areas as clean as possible (bring litter to designated bins).

- Only use what water is necessary.

- Keep the use of unnatural chemicals to a minimum. Avoid products that use CFCs (chlorofluorocarbons) as these harm the ozone layer.

- Don't leave all the lights switched on when rooms are not in use.

Thank you for your help, consideration and co-operation

DUNBRODY COOKERY SCHOOL

At Dunbrody County House Hotel, Arthurstown, Co. Wexford by Masterchef Kevin Dundon.

Dunbrody Cookery School has been designed to cater for all levels of cooks, from budding enthusiasts to the experienced gourmet. With groups of up to ten we offer guests the chance to translate their enthusiasm and love for food into the real skills needed to produce fantastic food. Our belief is that cooking should be fun and our courses are designed to be fun also.

Courses designed under the care and guidance of Masterchef Kevin Dundon will teach guests the secrets of producing fine food using only the best of quality Irish ingredients. The emphasis at Dunbrody Cookery School is on freshness of ingredients and utilising these to achieve fabulous dishes without the worry of overly-complicated recipes.

Courses range from one day demonstrations to one and two day residential programmes.

For further information please contact us:
T +353 (0) 51 389 600   F +353 (0)51 389 601
E dunbrody@indigo.ie   W www.dunbrodyhouse.com

Houses, Castles and Gardens of Ireland

Houses, Castles and Gardens of Ireland represents a broad selection of architectural gems. As well as the great Georgian buildings of the 18th century for which Ireland is renowned, there are other treasures to be visited. Early castle strongholds, gothic revival houses of the Victorian era, formal 17th century gardens, landscape parks of the 18th century, 20th century cottage gardens, townhouse gardens and botanic gardens and arboreta are all represented.

Visit our web site at www.castlesireland.com or www.gardensireland.com
Or email info@castlesireland.com or info@gardensireland.com for a free brochure/map

Heritage Island

is a group of the most prestigious Visitor Attractions and Heritage Towns in all of Ireland...

The centres range from historic houses, castles, heritage towns, monuments, museums, galleries, national parks, interpretative centres, gardens and theme parks.

Visitors can avail of big savings by displaying the *Heritage Island Explorer* coupon at any Heritage Island centre, which will entitle them to reduced admission, many two for one's and special offers...

HERITAGE ISLAND
EXPLORER

Display this coupon at any Heritage Island Centre
to qualify for reduced admission.

For full details on centres, opening times, discounts and special offers see Heritage Island Touring Guide 2004 available at Tourist Information Centres, nationwide.

Heritage Island
37 Main Street,
Donnybrook, Dublin 4
Tel: +353 1 260 0055   Fax: +353 1 260 0058
Email: heritage.island@indigo.ie
Web: www.heritageisland.com

www.heritageisland.com

TOURISM IRELAND

INTERNATIONAL OFFICES

BRITAIN
Tourism Ireland, Nations House,
103 Wigmore Street,
London SW1Y 4XT.
Tel: +44 207 518 0800
Email: info.gb@tourismireland.com

Scotland
James Millar House, 98 West George Street,
7th Floor, Glasgow G2 1PJ.
Tel: +44 141 572 4030
Email: infoglasgow@tourismireland.com

Austria
Tourism Ireland,
Libellenweg 1, A-1140 Vienna.
Tel: +43 1 914 1351
Email: info@irland-ferine.de

Belgium
Tourism Ireland,
Avenue Louise 327 Louizalaan,
1050 Brussels.
Tel: +32 2 643 2121
Email: info.be@tourismireland.com

Denmark/Norway
Tourism Ireland, "Klostergarden",
Amagertov 29B,3, DK1160 Copenhagen K.
Tel: +45 33 15 8045
Email: info@irland-turisme.dk

**Denmark / Norway and Iceland
(Trade Publications)**
Tourism Ireland, "Klostergarden",
Amagertov 29B,3, 1160 Copenhagen K.
Tel: 33 15 80 45
Email: infodk@tourismireland.com

Finland
Erottajankatu 7A PL33,
00130 Helsinki.
Tel: +358 9 608961
Email: info@irlanninmatkailu.com

France
Tourism Irlandais, 33 Rue de Miromesnil,
75008 Paris.
Tel: +33 1 53 43 12 24
Email: info@irlande-tourisme.fr

Germany
Gutleustrasse 32,
D60329 Frankfurt/Main.
Tel: 069 668 00950
Email: http://www.irland-urlaub.de

Italy
Turismo Irlandese,
Via Santa Maria Segreta 6,
20123 Milano.
Tel: +39 02 8690 543
Email: info@turismo.irlandese.it

The Netherlands
Ierland Toerisme, Spuistraat 104,
1012 VA Amsterdam.
Tel: +31 20 53 06 050
Email: info@ierland.nl

Spain
Turismo de Irlanda,
Paseo de la Castellana 46, 3™ Planta,
28046 Madrid.
Tel: +34 91 577 54 58
Email: ireland@ran.es

Sweden
Tourism Ireland, Stora Nygatan 40,
SE 111 27 Stockholm.
Tel: +46 8 662 8510
Email: info@irlandsinfo.com

Switzerland
Tourism Ireland, Mettlenstrasse 22,
CH 8142 Uitikon,
Tel: +41 1 401 5260
Email: irishtouristtboard@uitikon.ch

USA
Tourism Ireland, 345 Park Avenue,
New York, NY 10154.
Tel: +1 212 418 0800
Email: info@shamrock.org

CANADA
Tourism Ireland, 2 Bloor St. West,
Suite 1501, Toronto M4W 3E2.
Tel: +1 416 925 6368
Email: info@shamrock.org

SOUTH AFRICA
Tourism Ireland,
c/o Development Promotions, 7th Floor,
Everite House, 20 De Korte Street,
Braamfontein 2001, Gauteng, South Africa.
Tel: +27 11 339 48 65
Email: hfraser@tourismireland.com
        sales@dpgsa.co.za
Postal Address: PO Box 30615,
Braamfontein 2017, Gauteng, South Africa.

NEW ZEALAND
Tourism Ireland, 6 Floor, 18 Shortland St.,
Private Bag 92136, Auckland 1.
Tel: 09 977 2255
Email: ireland@walwor.co.nz

AUSTRALIA
Tourism Ireland, 5th Level,
36 Carrington St., Sydney, NSW 2000.
Tel: +61 2 92 99 6177
Email: info@tourismireland.com.au

JAPAN
Tourism Ireland, Woody 21,23, Aizumi-cho,
Shijuku-ku, Tokyo, 160-005, Japan.
Tel: 03 5367 6515
Fax: 03 5363 1118

Ireland

Reservations in N. America and Canada:
Tel: Toll Free 800-323-5463, E mail: usa@irelandsbluebook.com

Correspondence / Enquiries:
Ireland's Blue Book, 8 Mount Street Crescent, Dublin 2.
Tel: 00-353-(0)-6769914. **Fax:** 00-353-(0)-6314990.
E-Mail: mail@irelandsbluebook.com **Website:** www.irelandsbluebook.com

Discover the many facets of Europe

The European Federation was created with the objective of bringing together the top European national marketing associations. These 12 associations represent their countries' national cultural traditions, historic heritage and architecture.

This similarity of spirit, passion and authenticity brings to each of the establishments an incomparable charm and character.

From this base, it is possible to set off on a discovery of the multi-faceted European identity, by going from country to country, guided step-by-step by the Federation, certain that you will find in every Hotel, Castle, Manor or Country House the same original charm and a sense of historic preservation.

Every property within the European Federation reflects a diversity of style and character and guests will enjoy different experiences when travelling from country to country.

GAST IM SCHLOSS
Postfach 1428 · 65527 Niedernhausen
Germany.
Fon: +49 (0) 6127 / 999 098
Fax: +49 (0) 6127 / 920 822
Mail: info@gast-im-schloss.de
Web: www.gast-im-schloss.de

WELSH RAREBITS
Prince's Square, Montgomery,
Powys SY15 6PZ, Wales, U.K.
Tel: (01686) 668030
Fax: (01686) 668029
E-mail: info@rarebits.co.uk
Web Site: www.welsh.rarebits.co.uk

COUNTRYSIDE HOTELS
Box 69, SE-830 13 Are,
Sweden.
Tél: 46 647 50680
Fax: 46 647 51920
E-mail: info@countrysidehotels.se
Web Site: www.countrysidehotels.se

HOTEIS HERITAGE LISBOA
Tv. Salitre, 5,
1269-066 Lisboa *
Portugal
Tel: +351 213 218 200
Fax: +351 213 471 630
E-Mail: heritage.hotels@heritage.pt

IRELAND'S BLUE BOOK,
8 Mount Street Crescent,
Dublin 2, Ireland.
Tel: +353-(0)1-6769914.
Fax: +353-(0)1-6314990.
E-Mail: mail@irelandsbluebook.com
Web Site: www.irelandsbluebook.com

EUROPEAN FEDERATION

TRADITIONAL ACCOMMODATION AND HISTORIC HOUSES

SCHLOSSHOTELS HERRENHÄUSER IN ÖSTERREICH
und den ehemaligen kronlÄndern
Geschäftsstelle Head Office
Moosstrasse 60, A-5020 Salzburg - Austria
Tel: 43/662/83 06 81 41
Fax: 43/662/83 06 81 61
e.mail: office@schlosshotels.co.at
web site: www.schlosshotels.co.at

HOSTERIAS/HOSPEDERIAS REALES
Booking Central,
C/Frailes. 1
13320 Vva. de los infantes (Ciudad Real)
Tlfo./Fax: 0034/926 36 17 88
e-mail: hospbuscon@wanadoo.es
web site: turinet.net/empresa/hosteriasreales

DE HISTORISKE HOTELS NORWAY
Strandgaten 223,
P.O. Box 1940 Nordnes,
5817 Bergen, Norway.
Tel: +47 55 31 67 60
Fax: +47 55 31 91 01
e.mail: info@historiskehotel.no
Website: www.historiskehotel.no

ESTANCIAS DE ESPAÑA
Menéndez Pidal, 31. 28036 Madrid
Spain
Tel: 34 91 345 41 41
Fax: 34 91 3 45 51 74
e.mail: info@estancias.com
Dirección Internet: www.estancias.com

ABITARE LA STORIA
Localita l'Amorosa - 53048 Sinalunga
Siena, Italy.
Tel: +39-0577-679683
Fax: +39-0577-632160
e.mail: mailbox@abitarelastoria.it
website: www.abitarelastoria.it

POUSADAS DE PORTUGAL
Avenida Santa Joana Princesa, 10
1749 - 090 Lisboa - Portugal
Tel: + 351 21 844 20 01
Fax: + 351 21 844 20 85
e.mail: Guest@pousadas.pt
website: www.pousadas.pt

PRIDE OF BRITAIN
Cowage Farm, Foxley,
Wilts. SN160JH, England
Tel: 01 666 824 666
Fax: 01 666 825 779
e.mail: info@prideofbritainhotels.com
website: www.prodeofbritainhotels.com

CHÂTEAUX ET HÔTELS DE FRANCE
30, rue des Jeûneurs
75002 PARIS
Tél: +33 (0)1 55 34 16 16
Fax: +33 (0)1 55 34 16 26
e-mail: resa@chateauxhotels.co
website: www.chateauxhotels.com

PRIDE OF BRITAIN
HOTELS

A COLLECTION OF THE FINEST
PRIVATELY OWNED HOTELS IN BRITAIN

For reservations in the UK please call +44 (0) 870 609 3012
From the USA call Toll Free 1-800 98 PRIDE
or visit www.prideofbritainhotels.com

Portfolio

COUNTRY PLACES
AND SAFARI COLLECTION

Portfolio's Country Places and Safari Collection is one of a
series of select guides for the discerning traveller, offering
fine Country Houses, Hotels and Private Game Reserves
in Southern Africa.

THE PORTFOLIO COLLECTION
SINCE 1982

Benchmark of the Best

Online Reservations www.portfoliocollection.com

SOUTH AFRICA ONLINE RESERVATIONS OFFICE
Tel (++27) (11) 880 3414 Fax (++27) (11) 788 4802
e-mail : res@portfoliocollection.com
UK RESERVATIONS OFFICE - AFRICA COLLECTION LTD
Tel (01403) 256 655 Fax (01403) 253 325
e-mail : info@africacollection.com